CW00649513

Pole Dancing Fitness Syllabus

The Pole Dance Community Syllabus – 2013

Copyright © 2012 by Pole Dance Community.
All rights reserved.

No part of this publication may be reproduced, distributed,
or transmitted in any form or by any means, including photocopying,
recording, or other electronic or mechanical methods, without the prior written
permission of the publishers. For permission requests, write to the publishers
at the address below.

The PDC Team
Pole Dance Community
5, Beaumont Avenue
Greenbank
Plymouth
Devon UK
PL4 8DX

Ordering Information:
Quantity sales. Special discounts are available on quantity purchases by
corporations, associations, and others. For details, contact the authors at the
address above.

ISBN 978-0-9571678-34

Dedications

Thanks to all the PDC Approved instructors who have helped make this syllabus possible.

The instructors listed below are those demonstrating the moves in this book and those on the Syllabus Steering Group. They have given up their time, and in some cases their studio, to help compile the syllabus. They attended the various filming days held across the UK throughout 2011/12

Dancers

Alex Conley
Amy Williams
Anne Goswell
Claire Rigby
Emily Smith
Dancers
Emma Thorpe
Kate Johnstone
Leana Darbyshire
Lucy KingMichaela
RobertsMiranda
GoldringNadine
Blacow
Robyn Rooke
Rosanna Durban
Rose Wallace
Sam Remmer
Sarah Scott
Shelly Neave

Syllabus Steering Group

Alex Conley
Ally Frankilin
Julie Stewart
Mary Ellyn Weissman
Mikal Mount
Natasha Williams
Robyn Rooke
Sam Remmer
Sid Remmer
Sophie Herrmann
Suzie Q

Credit to the cover model, Lucy Webster of Inversion Pole Fitness.

Thanks to Sid Remmer for compiling the book and recording the images.

PDC Pole Dance Fitness Syllabus

This book is made by pole dancers for pole dancers.

It is the collaborative work of over 300 PDC Approved pole dancing instructors who have submitted their pole dancing tricks, spins and combinations to the constantly evolving PDC Syllabus.

Featuring over 3000 images we hope this will help both students and instructors to understand and breakdown the techniques.

Our members have also added their AKA's so each move has a most commonly used name as well as other names currently in use.

Each move is labelled with its level of difficulty – these levels relate to the PDC pole dancer grading system - the Advancement and Accreditation Program.

Details of the scheme and how to join in can be found at the back of this book.

The PDC Syllabus was not primarily designed as a teaching aid, rather it is a resource to help the development of pole dance grading and to provide a reference point for names and the classification of moves.

We hope you will find this book useful to chart your pole dancing progress, ticking off moves you have successfully achieved and making notes about moves that need further development.

We wish you every success with your pole dancing progression.

Level 1

A Frame (facing away from pole)

Also known as:

Forward Fold, Hamstring Stretch, Forward Bend, Pole Caress

PDC Notes

Your Notes

A Frame (facing pole)

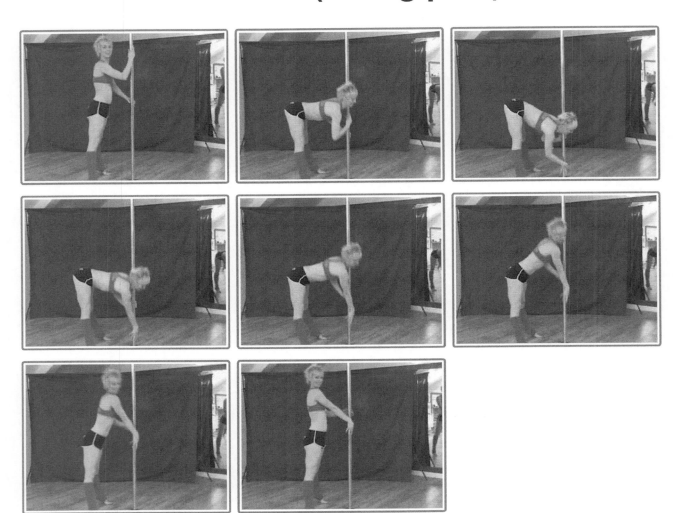

Also known as:

Forward Fold, Hamstring Stretch, Forward Bend, Pole Caress

PDC Notes

Good hamstring stretch. Great preparation for Hands Free Handstand, then progress to the Iguana.

Your Notes

Back Arch

Also known as:

Crab Slide.

PDC Notes

Bicep lock to protect lumbar. Wide foot stance recommended.

Your Notes

Back Hook Spin

Also known as:

Showgirl Spin, Dizzy Spin

PDC Notes

Keep slight arch on back, knees wide apart, toes pointed. Use 2 handed baseball grip.

Your Notes

Backslide (one leg extended)

Also known as:

Bunny Slide, Pole Drop

PDC Notes

Watch out for hyper-extension on the knees, try keeping one foot forward to help stability.

Your Notes

Backwards Pole Switch

Also known as:

Step Behind Turn

PDC Notes

Work through the balls of the feet and extend through the spine for good posture

Your Notes

Ballet Hook

Also known as:

Flamingo, Ballerina

PDC Notes

Strong hip work move, works gluts and adductors. Good for balance, flexibility and developing a strong knee hold.

Your Notes

Basic Fireman

Also known as:

Close Contact Spin, Fireman Spin

PDC Notes

Nice beginner's spin ideal for static or spinning pole. Once you have mastered this you can try it one handed by taking your lower hand off the pole.

Your Notes

Body Wave

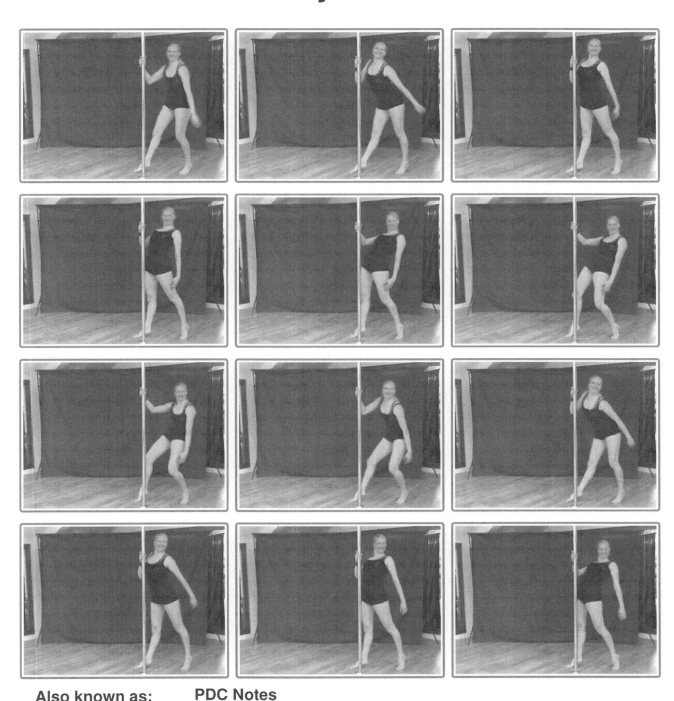

Also known as:

Body Roll

PDC Notes

Perfect for improving body isolation and general body awareness. Work through the balls of the feet to help tone the calf muscles.

Your Notes

Body Wave Kick

Also known as:

Body Roll variation

PDC Notes

Nice transitional move. Remember to point your toes!

Your Notes

Bounce to Side Step

Also known as:

Spring and Slide, Bounce to Feet, Recovery Postition, Prima Rise, Jump Up, Bobbi Rise

PDC Notes

Good Hamstring stretch and you can add a head flick to the end for dramatic effect

Your Notes

Cat Crawl

Also known as:
Panther Crawl.

PDC Notes
Handy move for travelling from 1 pole to another in a routine.

Your Notes

Crucifix

Also known as:

PDC Notes

Pressure to upper foot. Lean into pole to increase grip.

Your Notes

Dip to Wraparound

Also known as:

Dip to Heron, Dip to Step Around

PDC Notes

Nice gentle leg exercise

Your Notes

Eternal Pole Walks

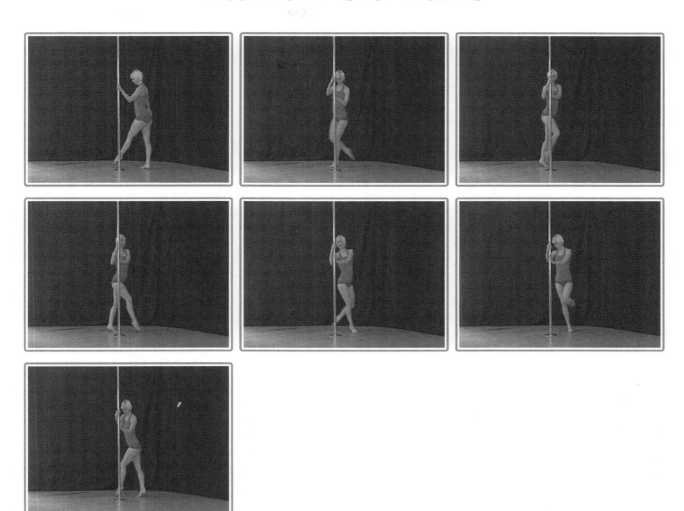

Also known as:

PDC Notes

Your Notes

Fireman Spin Crossed Leg Closed

Also known as:

PDC Notes
Master this spin first before trying the one handed version.

Fireman Spin Crossed leg Open

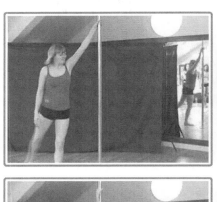  

Also known as:

PDC Notes

Master the two handed version first.

Floor Back Arch

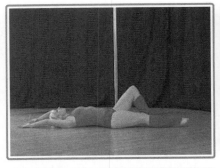 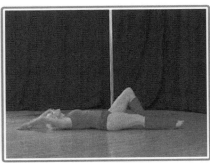 

Also known as:

Floor Trucker Pose, Suntan, Floor Model Pose.

PDC Notes

Don't over-arch the back unless you have the flexibility to do so.

Your Notes

Floor Fan

Also known as:

Pin-up Girl.

PDC Notes

Try the side spin first to get you onto the floor.

Your Notes

Floor Fan Kick

Also known as:

Floor Fan Cartwheel, Floor Fan Circle

PDC Notes

Remember to point your toes

Your Notes

Floor Inversion

Also known as:

Shoulder Stand

PDC Notes

Strong neck stretch but nice for stretching out the lower back by bringing the legs down towards the floor. Progress to Floor Inversion Sit-Up, Floor Inversion Repeaters and Backward Rolls.

Your Notes

Forwards Body Slide

 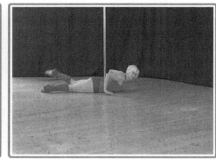 

Also known as:

Panther, Back Body Wave

PDC Notes

Try also Reverse Body Slide.

Your Notes

Forwards Pole Switch

Also known as:

Step Across Turn, Step Forwards Turn, Pass in front

PDC Notes

Try the Backwards Pole Switch also.

Your Notes

High Hand Pirouette (one handed)

Also known as:

Walking Circles

PDC Notes

Work through the balls of the feet and extend through the spine for good posture.

Your Notes

High Hand Pirouette (two handed)

Also known as:

PDC Notes

There are lots of ways to execute Pirouettes. Find the most comfortable technique for you to ensure grace and fluidity.

Your Notes

Knee Circles (both)

Also known as:

Clock, Clock Hands

PDC Notes
Nice abdominal workout, don't forget to point the toes!
Lovely for the quads too.

Lateral Stretch

Also known as:

Flamingo

PDC Notes

Lovely stretch for the oblique muscles. Repeat for oblique conditioning. Try varying your hands and arms to make creative shapes. You can bend either knee.

Your Notes

Log Roll (1)

Also known as:

Floor Roll

PDC Notes

Nice beginners move for building core and upper body strength. Once this is comfortable try Log Roll (2)

Your Notes

Log Roll (2)

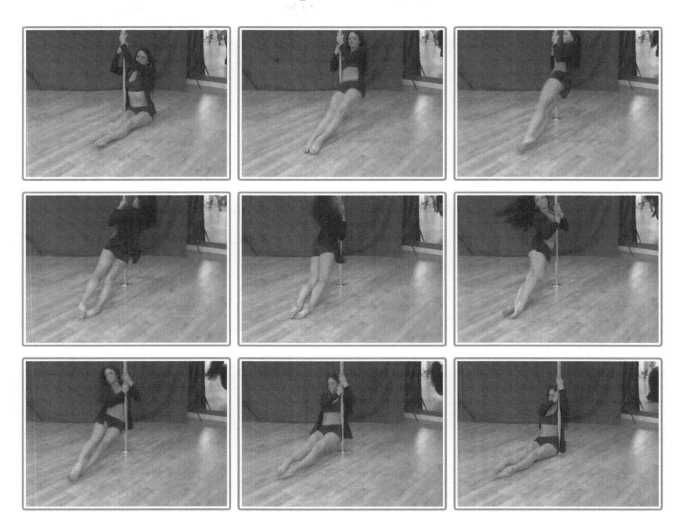

Also known as:

Floor Roll

PDC Notes

Nice beginners move for building core strength. Master the Log Roll (1) first before attempting this.

Your Notes

Pirouette (elbow grip)

Also known as:
Elbow Walk

PDC Notes
Risk of bruising/abrasion to elbow pit.

Your Notes

Pirouette (low hand)

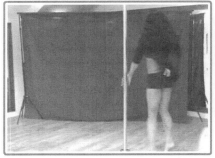  

Also known as:

Spinning Pole Walk

PDC Notes

This move may make you dizzy! The faster you execute the more impressive it can look. Work through the balls of your feet.

Your Notes

Pole Peek

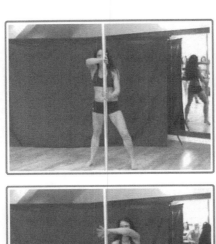  

Also known as:

PDC Notes
Great transitional move.
Keep a nice wide stance.

Your Notes

Pole Walk

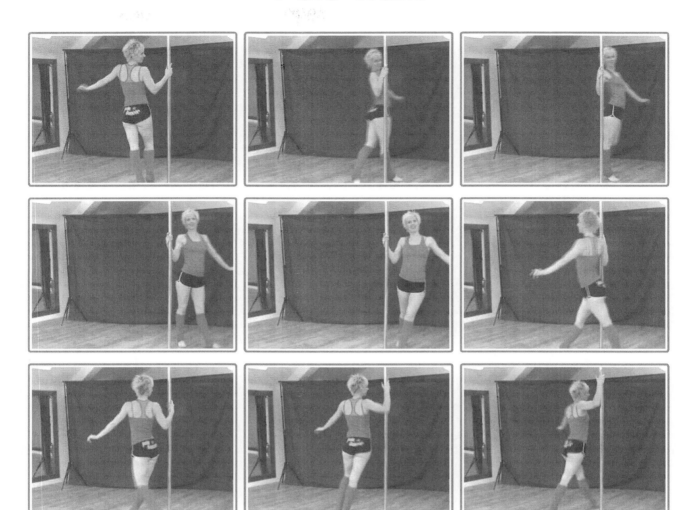

Also known as:

PDC Notes

Ensure execution is perfect with good posture and by walking through the balls of the feet.

Your Notes

Pole Walk Repeaters

Also known as:

Half Turn, Half Pirouette, Step and Turn

PDC Notes

A lovely transitional move.

Your Notes

Reverse Body Slide

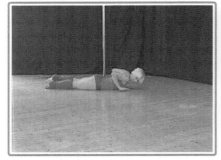  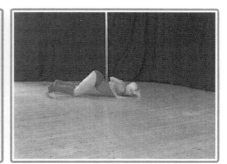

Also known as:

Panther, Back Body Wave

PDC Notes

Your Notes

Reverse High Hand Pirouette

Also known as:

Reverse Walking Circles

PDC Notes

Your Notes

Rock n Roll

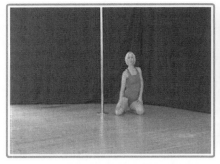  

Also known as:

Peek a Boo

PDC Notes

Your Notes

Step Around

Also known as:

Dips, Leg Circles

PDC Notes

Your Notes

Tango Kick

Also known as:

Exotic Kick, Ballerina Kick

PDC Notes

Nice way to work the hips. This kick is very versatile so you can adapt it to suit your music and style.

Your Notes

Wrap Around

Also known as:

Step and Hook

PDC Notes

Perfect move for beginners. Ensure toes are pointed and posture is good.

Your Notes

Level 2

Attitude Spin (half bracket grip)

Also known as:

Sunwheel Spin.

PDC Notes

This variation is easier on the lower arm than the Attitude Spin (bracket grip). Ensure good alignment through the legs.

Your Notes

Backward Floor Roll

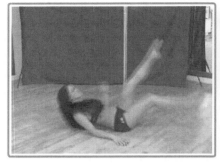  

Also known as:

Backwards Roly Poly

PDC Notes

Neck pressure involved on roll through. A head flick can be added to the end of the roll for dramatic effect.

Your Notes

Ball

  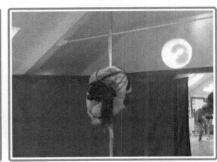

Also known as:

Seated Crouch, Drama Queen,

PDC Notes

Start with Straight Leg Seat, some people prefer to cross their legs the opposite way to their preferred grip for this move.

Your Notes

Chair Spin (half bracket grip)

Also known as:

Carousel Spin

PDC Notes

Ideal for those who don't like the full bracket variation.

Your Notes

Crab Spin

Also known as:

Basic Straddle, Basic Boomerang, Baby Boomerang, Basic Barbie, Straddle Prep
Spin

PDC Notes

Your Notes

Cradle Spin (reverse baseball grip)

Also known as:

Tuck Spin, Cradle Spin, Barbed Wire Spin

PDC Notes

Ensure you get lots of momentum for this spin. Keep top arm bent.

Your Notes

Cross Ankle Sit

Also known as:

Pole sit, Cross Ankle Seat

PDC Notes

Pole burn to thighs to be expected when first attempting!

Your Notes

Cross Ankle Sit (one handed)

Also known as:

Pole Sit

PDC Notes

Expect burning to the inner thighs when learning. Progress to no handed variations.

Your Notes

Cross Knee Sit

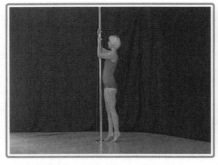  

Also known as:

Pole Sit, Seat

PDC Notes

Your Notes

Cross Knee Sit (one handed)

Also known as:

Pole Sit, Seat

PDC Notes

Your Notes

Cross Knee Sit Preparation

Also known as:

PDC Notes

Your Notes

Crucifix Forward Fold

Also known as:

Crucifix Forward Fold

PDC Notes

Master the Crucifix and Crucifix Twist first. Ensure good skin contact on legs and abdomen.

Your Notes

Crucifix Twist

Also known as:

Titanic,

PDC Notes

Once you have mastered the Crucifix you can try this move. You can also add a full forward fold by taking the head down onto the knee i.e Bow.

Your Notes

Fireman Spin (one leg straight)

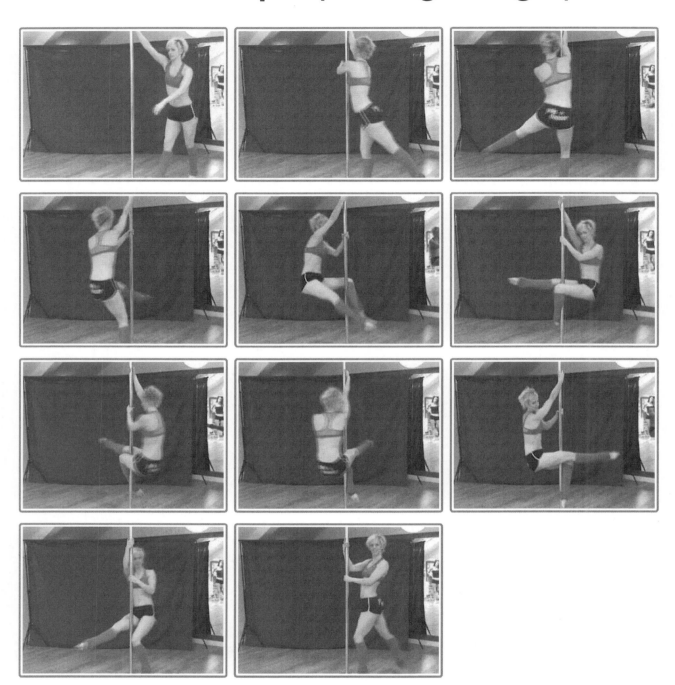

Also known as:

Half Pike Spin.

PDC Notes

Keep one leg bent and one leg fully extended. Once you have mastered this try the one handed Fireman variations.

Your Notes

Fireman Spin Crossed Leg Open (one handed)

Also known as:

PDC Notes

Master the two handed version first.

Your Notes

Floor Inversion Repeaters

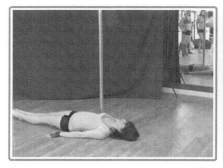
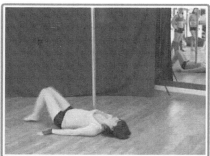

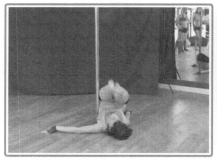

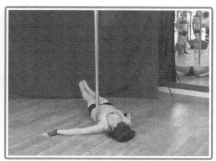

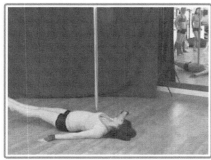

Also known as:

Shoulder Stand variation

PDC Notes

Nice abdominal toning exercise.

Front Hook Spin (two handed)

Also known as:

Swan Slide Spinner, Butterfly Spin, Vanessa, Forwards Vanessa.

PDC Notes

For perfect execution arch the back and push the pelvis forward whilst pushing the knees apart and pointing the toes.

Your Notes

Front Hook to Back Hook Spin (two handed)

Also known as:
Swan Slide Spinner to Reverse Swan Slide Spinner, Butterfly Spin to Reverse Butterfly Spin, Forward Vanessa to Backward vanessa.

PDC Notes
Master the Front Hook Spin (two handed) and Back Hook Spin (two handed) first. Watch your outside knee does not bash into the pole as you switch from the front hook to back hook.

Half Front Hook Spin (two handed)

Also known as:

Front hook Extended Leg, Vanessa Extended Leg

PDC Notes

Nice way to work towards full spins. Once you have mastered this try the Front Hook Spin (two handed).

Headstand (bow and arrow legs)

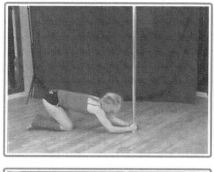  

Also known as:

Elbow Stand

PDC Notes

Be aware of pressure to the neck when performing headstands. Ensure good alignment through the legs and be aware of how long you remain inverted!

Your Notes

Headstand (prayer legs)

Also known as:

Elbow Stand

PDC Notes

Be aware of pressure to the neck and back when performing this headstand. Ensure good alignment through the legs and be aware of how long you remain inverted!

Your Notes

Hollywood Spin

Also known as:
Inside Hook Spin, Half Attitude Spin

PDC Notes
Hook inside leg on the pole and fully extend your outside leg.

Hollywood Spin (no hook)

Also known as:

Half Attitude Spin

PDC Notes

Place inside knee on the pole and fully extend your outside leg.

Jumping Back Hook Spin (two handed)

Also known as:

Dizzy Spin variation

PDC Notes
Try also the Back Hook
Spin (two handed).

Layout

Also known as:

Layback, Lean Back, Advanced Plank

PDC Notes

Ensure full extension through the body.

Your Notes

Mermaid Spin

Also known as:

Pike Spin Drop

PDC Notes

Master the Fireman Spin (straight legs) first before attempting this interesting variation.

Your Notes

Side Spin (two handed baseball grip)

Also known as:

Gabrielle Spin

PDC Notes

Your Notes

Side Spin (two handed)

Also known as:

Gabrielle Spin

PDC Notes

Your Notes

Spinning Step Around

Also known as:

Spinning Leg Circles

PDC Notes

Nice way to work towards more advanced spins or to lead into another spin such as the Back Hook Spin (two handed).

Your Notes

Upright Thigh Hold

Also known as:

Angel, Crucifix Leg Extension, Standing Thigh Seat

PDC Notes

Perfect progression from Crucifix. Try also climbing spins.

Your Notes

Level 3

Apprentice

Also known as:

Anchor, Basic Jamilla, Basic Hero, Advanced Jamilla, Side Mount

PDC Notes

Allegra amount of pressure to lower forearm/wrist, top arm should be bent and low.

Your Notes

Archer

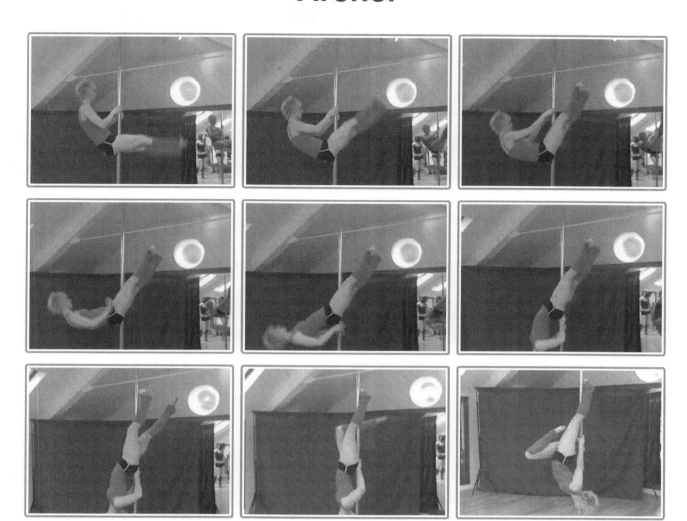

Also known as:
Basic Bow and Arrow, Flying Bat

PDC Notes
Master the Bat first. Ensure good hand grip and skin contact on top of foot.

Your Notes

Attitude Spin (bracket grip)

Also known as:
Sunwheel Spin.

PDC Notes
Pretty spin that can be taken down to the floor or stepped out off.

Your Notes

Attitude Spin-up

Also known as:

Seated Spinner Ascent, Sunwheel Ascent

PDC Notes

As Attitude Spin but from the floor.

Your Notes

Back Hook Spin (one handed)

Also known as:

Showgirl, Backwards Vanessa, Dizzy

PDC Notes

1 handed variation, keep slight arch on back, knees wide apart, toes pointed.

Your Notes

Basic Archer

Also known as:

Bow and Arrow Variation, Flying Bat

PDC Notes

Master the Bat first then progress towards more advanced moves such as Archer and Iguana variations

Your Notes

Basic Climb

  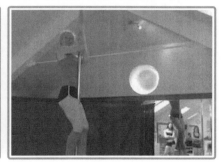

Also known as:

Monkey Climb Variation, Show Climb, Basic Climb Variation

PDC Notes

Master the Crucifix first.

Your Notes

Basic Invert

Also known as:

Alley Oop, Classic Invert.

PDC Notes

Once you have mastered this, you can progress to the Inverted Crucifix.

Your Notes

Butterfly

  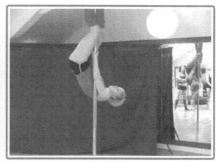

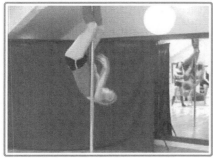  

  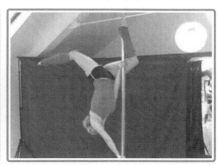

Also known as:

Lotus, Venus, Papillion

PDC Notes

Ideal progression from invert. Strong bracket grip required.

Your Notes

Butterfly Handstand

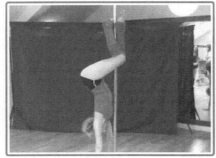  

Also known as:

Split Leg Hook,

PDC Notes

Pretty Handstand variation. Nice way to learn the leg contact needed for the Butterfly.

Your Notes

Cartwheel Spin

Also known as:

Windmill Spin

PDC Notes

Ensure good alignment through legs. Link and repeat spin for dramatic effect.

Your Notes

Cartwheel Spin (bracket grip)

Also known as:

Windmill Spin

PDC Notes

Try repeating this spin for dramatic effect. Ensure good alignment through legs.

Your Notes

Cartwheel Spin to Sit

Also known as:

Windmill Spin to Pole Sit,

PDC Notes

Master the Cartwheel Spin and Seat individually first then try linking. You can then try the Aerial version of this combination.

Your Notes

Chair Spin (bracket grip)

Also known as:

Carousel Spin.

PDC Notes

Watch for pressure on lower wrist. Point toes throughout.

Your Notes

Chair Spin to Reverse Chair Spin

Also known as:
Carousel Spin to Reverse
Carousel Spin.

PDC Notes
Master the Chair Spin first before trying this lovely
variation.

Your Notes

Chaundy Climb

Also known as:

Monkey Climb Variation.

PDC Notes

When learning keep a bend on the elbows with the hands placed lower rather than over stretching to reach into the climb. Repeat the climb for strength training and visual effect.

Your Notes

Climbing Fireman

Also known as:

Climbing Spin

PDC Notes

Perfect progression from fireman spin. Can bruise/burn upper foot. Good for building upper body strength.

Your Notes

Climbing Spin

Also known as:

Fairy Spin

PDC Notes

Perfect progression from fireman spin. Can bruise/burn upper foot. Good for building upper body strength.

Your Notes

Cobra Dismount

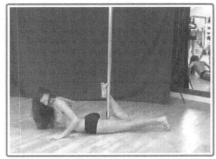  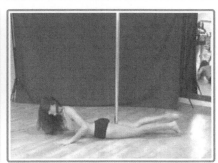

Also known as:

Invert Dismount, Belly Slide.

PDC Notes

Be aware of pressure to lower back and upper foot. Good for wrist strengthening. Now work on the Swan Dive.

Your Notes

Corkscrew Spin (two handed)

Also known as:

Helter Skelter Spin,

PDC Notes

Once you have mastered this spin you can try the one-handed and no-handed variations. You can execute the spin with either hand at the top.

Your Notes

Cradle Position (bow and arrow legs bracket grip)

Also known as:

Barbed wire variation, Dropped Cradle, Crouch Pose

PDC Notes

Your Notes

Cradle Spin (knees tucked bracket grip)

Also known as:

Barbed Wire Spin, Side Spiral, Cradle Spin

PDC Notes

Be aware of pressure to lower wrist.

Your Notes

Cradle Spin (one leg bent one leg straight)

Also known as:
Tuck Spin, Crouch Spin,
Barbed Wire Spin

PDC Notes
You can bend either leg.
Ensure the toes are pointed
throughout this pretty spin.

Your Notes

Cradle Spin (straddle legs)

Also known as:

Barbed Wire Straddle, Side Spiral Straddle, Cradle Straddle

PDC Notes

Progress to Anchor and Jamilla poses.

Your Notes

Cradle Spin-up

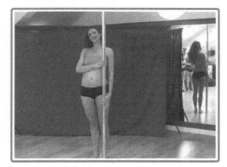

Also known as:
Barbed Wire Ascent, Low Lift Spin, Side Spiral ascent, Cradle ascent

PDC Notes
Progress to Cradle Poses and Anchor.

Your Notes

Cross Ankle Release

Also known as:

Dropback, Fantasy, Vamp, Hangback, Cross Ankle Release, Fang, Hang Back,

PDC Notes

Ensure tight grip between thighs and squeeze knees and ankles together to avoid the pole slipping through your grip.

Your Notes

Cross Knee Release

Also known as:

Cross Knee Release

PDC Notes

Learn close to the floor before trying at height. Master the Seat variations first.

Your Notes

Dolphin Spin (closed)

PDC Notes

Risk of pressure to lower back. Ensure there is plenty of space around your pole.

Embrace

Also known as:

Elbow Hold Hangman.

PDC Notes

Ensure good elbow grip and expect to experience pain, bruising and skin abrasion in the elbow pit when learning.

Your Notes

Extended Backward Floor Roll

Also known as:

Posh Roly Poly

PDC Notes

Lots of pressure to neck! Ensure good, clean floor surface.

Your Notes

Fairy Walk

Also known as:

One Handed Lift Spin

PDC Notes

Keep this move light through the balls of the feet.

Your Notes

Figurehead (two handed)

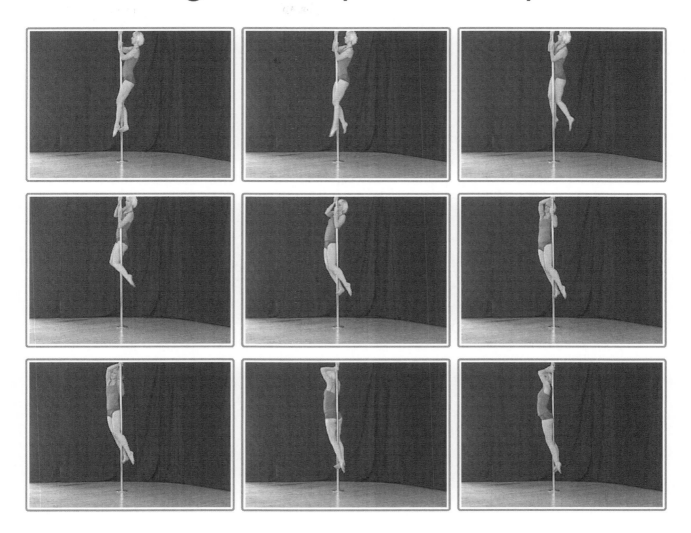

Also known as:

Statue, Titanic, Crescent Moon.

PDC Notes

Ideal transition from Side Climb. Progress to Figurehead (one handed) and Air Shoulder Mount.

Your Notes

Fireman Spin (both legs straight)

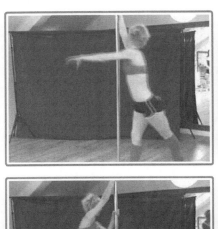  

Also known as:

Pike Spin.

PDC Notes

Straight leg - two handed - baseball grip, progress to 1 handed.

Your Notes

Floor Star

Also known as:

Pelvic Lift

PDC Notes

Nice piece of floor work and a good training exercise, remember to work both sides of the body.

Your Notes

Flying Back Hook Spin

PDC Notes

Try Jumping Back Hook first. Lots of momentum required to execute this spin well.

Front Hook Spin (one handed)

Also known as:
Swan Slide Spinner,
Butterfly Spin, Vanessa,
Forwards Vanessa.

PDC Notes
Master the Front Hook Spin
(two handed) first. For perfect
execution arch the back and
push the pelvis forward whilst
pushing the knees apart and
pointing the toes.

Your Notes

Front Hook to Back Hook Spin (one handed)

Also known as:

Swan Slide Spinner to Reverse Swan Slide Spinner, Butterfly Spin to Reverse Butterfly Spin, Forward Vanessa to Backward Vanessa

PDC Notes

Master the Front Hook Spin (one handed) and Back Hook Spin (one handed) first. Watch your outside knee does not bash into the pole as you switch from the Front Hook Spin to the Back Hook Spin.

Your Notes

Gemini (one handed)

Also known as:

Scorpio (one handed), Closed Scorpio, Closed Gemini, Inside Leg Hook, Inside Leg Hang.

PDC Notes

Once you have mastered this try the other no handed Gemini variations. Ensure good skin contact with inner leg (calf muscle and inner thigh) as well as abdomen.

Your Notes

Half Snake Spin

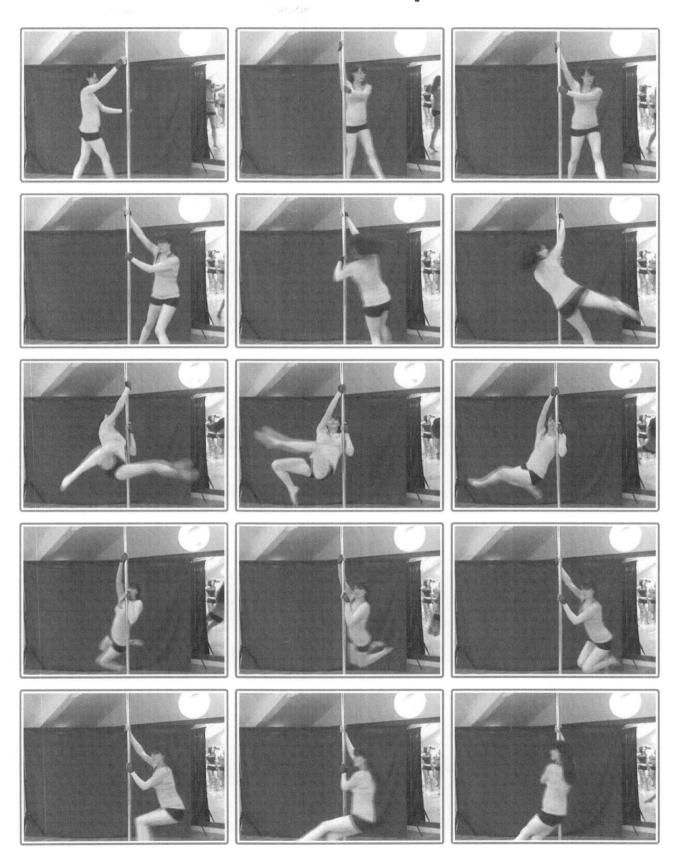

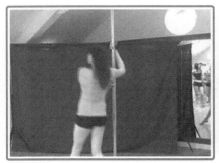 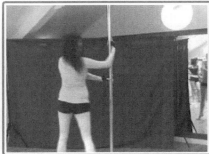 

Also known as:

Black Widow Spin variation

PDC Notes

Once you have mastered this try the Snake Spin.

Your Notes

Handspring Preparation

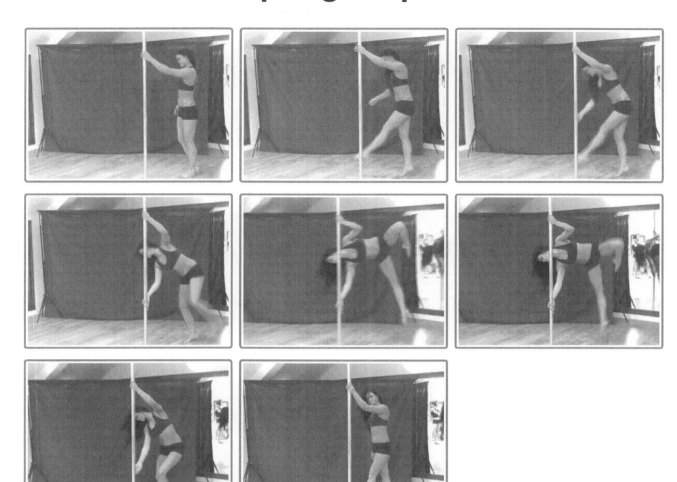

Also known as:

Elena Kick

PDC Notes

Perfect preparation for Parallel Handstands. Can use twisted grip, cup grip or classic grip.

Your Notes

Handspring Preparation (extended legs)

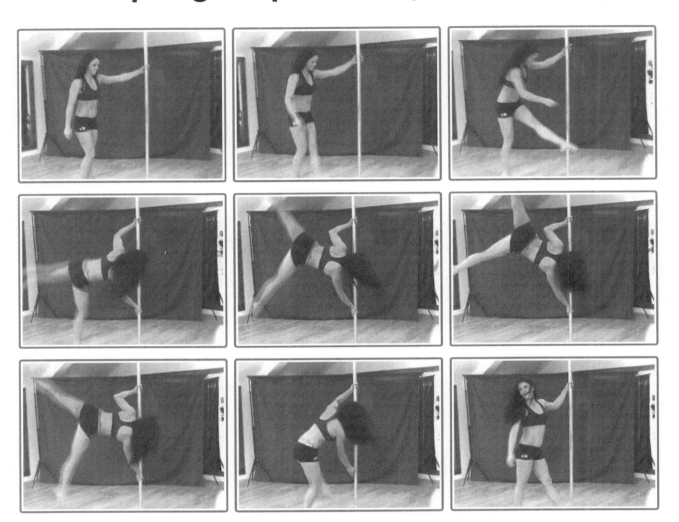

Also known as:

Elena Kick

PDC Notes

Perfect preparation for Parallel Handstands. Can use twisted grip, cup grip or classic grip.

Your Notes

Handstand (into pole)

Also known as:

PDC Notes

Ensure you place your hands in the right position so that you catch the pole with your back. You may find it helps to hook one foot onto the pole to help you centre yourself.

Your Notes

Hollywood Spin (one handed)

Also known as:

Fireman Split Spin

PDC Notes

Make sure the toes are pointed on both feet.

Your Notes

Hood Ornament

Also known as:

Helms Pose

PDC Notes

Arch the back for maximum effect. Ensure good skin contact on the inner arm and legs.

Your Notes

Inverted Crucifix

PDC Notes

Learn the Basic Invert and Crucifix first so you have a good knowledge of how to get upside down and where your legs should be positioned.

Your Notes

Inverted Thigh Hold

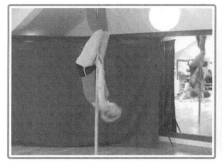  

  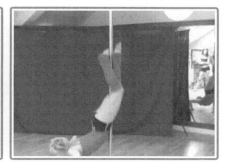

Also known as:

Tammy, Mantis Variation

PDC Notes

Ensure good skin contact on thigh and back of calf.

Your Notes

Jumping Straddle Spin

 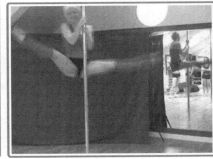 

Also known as:

Jumping Straddle Spin

PDC Notes

Master the Boomerang Spin (half bracket) first.

Your Notes

Liberty

Also known as:

Flatline Cross Knee Layback

PDC Notes

Try also the Seated Fall Back then progress to the Plank and Bat variations.

Your Notes

Passe Spin

Also known as:

Tinkerbell Spin

PDC Notes

Be aware of pressure to the lower wrist and don't forget to point your toes

Your Notes

Pencil Spin

  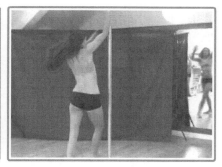

  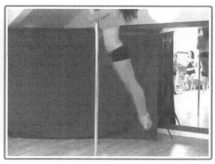

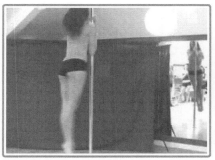  

Also known as:

Vertical Spin, Straight Spin

PDC Notes

Looks fabulous on a spinning pole. Try also the Scissor Spin.

Your Notes

Peter Pan

Also known as:

Seated Twist, Advanced Seat

PDC Notes

Master the Seat first. Good skin contact required on upper, inner thighs.

Your Notes

Pike Spin

Also known as:

Chair Spin (stretched legs), Concorde Spin

PDC Notes

Your Notes

Plank (one handed)

Also known as:

Superman Reverse

PDC Notes

Try also the Liberty and Layout.

Your Notes

Plank (two handed)

Also known as:

Flatliner, Layout

PDC Notes

Once you have mastered this try the Plank (one handed) and Advanced Layback variations.

Your Notes

Reiko Splits (two handed)

Also known as:

Reiko Stretch, Chinese Pole Stretch

PDC Notes

Once you have mastered this you can try the one handed variation. Can be used as a great pole assisted stretch.

Your Notes

Reverse Attitude Spin

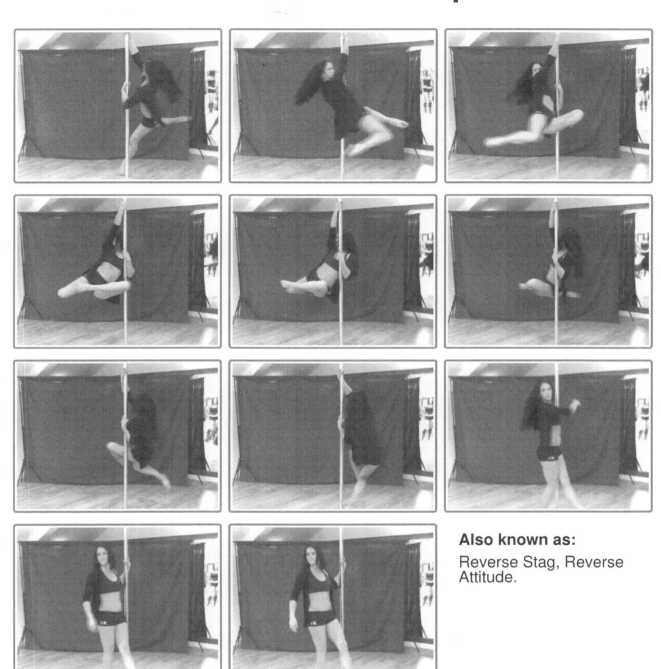

Also known as:

Reverse Stag, Reverse Attitude.

PDC Notes

Lots of momentum needed, slight arch to back. Risk of bashing ribs and inner arm.

Your Notes

Reverse Attitude Spin (half bracket grip)

Also known as:

Showgirl Variation, Black Widow Spin

PDC Notes

Lots of momentum needed. Risk of bashing ribs and inner arm bruising.

Your Notes

Rockstar Spin

Also known as:

Fireman Split Spin

PDC Notes

Make sure the toes are pointed on both feet.

Your Notes

Scissor Spin

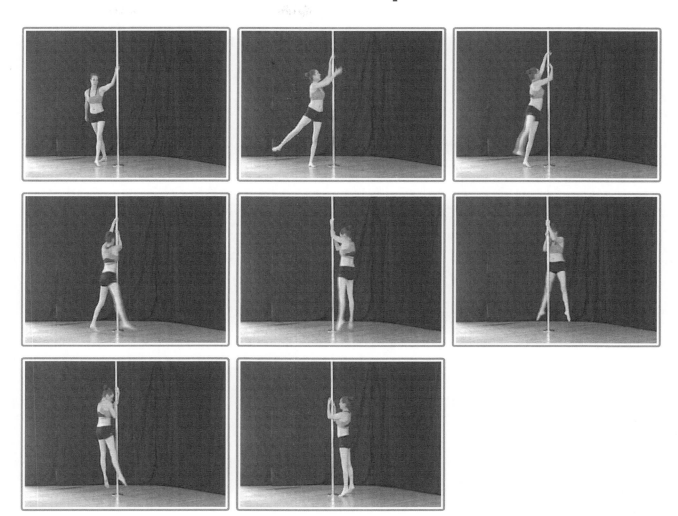

Also known as:

Broken Pencil Spin, Ballerina Spin

PDC Notes

Looks impressive on a spinning pole.

Your Notes

Shoulder Mount Preparation (scissor kick)

Also known as:

Backward Kick Split

PDC Notes

Good way to build strength ready for Shoulder Mounts. Helps build triceps and core strength.

Your Notes

Shoulder Mount Preparation (straddle legs)

Also known as:

Boomerang Pose, Shoulder Mount Straddle

PDC Notes

Excellent conditioning for abs and triceps, good shoulder mount training move.

Your Notes

Shoulder Roll Dismount

Also known as:

PDC Notes

Nice way to dismount from the pole. Try the Swan Dive too.

Your Notes

Skater (elbow hold)

Also known as:

PDC Notes

Try also the Skater (forearm grip) and progress to the Chinese Skater.

Your Notes

Skater (forearm grip)

Also known as:

PDC Notes

Try the Skater (elbow hold) and progress to the Chinese Skater.

Your Notes

Straddle Spin (baseball grip)

Also known as:
Boomerang Spin, Anchor Spin

PDC Notes
Ensure good core and upper body strength so your pelvis does not collide with the pole.

Straddle Spin (half bracket grip)

Also known as:
Boomerang Spin, Anchor Spin

PDC Notes
Good leg flexibility required. Ensure you point your toes!

Your Notes

Straddle Spin-up

Also known as:

Boomerang Spin-up, Anchor Spin-up

PDC Notes

Master the Boomerang Spin first before trying the Spin-up as it requires more upper body strength.

Your Notes

Switcharoo Spin

Also known as:
Hollywood Spin to Attitude Spin.

PDC Notes
Master the Hollywood Spin and Attitude Spin first then try this lovely combination.

Your Notes

Western Flag (one leg bent)

Also known as:

Flag variation.

PDC Notes

Once you have mastered this try the Western Flag.

Your Notes

Woodpecker

Also known as:

Cuckoo

PDC Notes

Good thigh and elbow conditioning.

Your Notes

Wrist Sit

Also known as:

PDC Notes

Be aware of pressure to lower forearm.

Your Notes

Level 4

Air Apprentice

Also known as:

Air Side V

PDC Notes

Apprentice can also be executed with the bottom knee bent and top ankle placed on the pole. Great move for getting into Jamilla and Extended Butterfly.

Air Invert

Also known as:

climb to invert, Super Invert, Aerial Invert.

PDC Notes

Good core and upper body strength required, master the Basic Invert first before attempting this.

Your Notes

Anchor Lift

Also known as:

Pencil lift.

PDC Notes

Point the toes when executing this pretty lift. If the lower arm feels comfortable in this move try the Apprentice variations too.

Your Notes

Angel Pose (closed)

Also known as:

Armpit Hold, Reverse Rocket Man.

PDC Notes

You may experience discomfort on the inner arm when learning. Good core strength required.

Your Notes

Angel Pose (open)

Also known as:

Armpit Hold, Reverse Rocket Man.

PDC Notes

You may experience discomfort on the inner arm when learning. Good upper body and core strength required.

Your Notes

Blade

Also known as: Mantis Variation, Top Handed Viva

PDC Notes
This is a beautiful outside knee hook. Try also moves such as the Mantis, Tammy, Teapot and Aerial Climb. Images show a Chopper before the Blade pose.

Your Notes

Bomb (closed)

Also known as:

Inverted Ball.

PDC Notes

Try also the Bomb (closed). You can move from the Bomb into moves such as the Pike, Hands Free Chopper or Jade.

Your Notes

Bomb (open)

Also known as:

Inverted Ball.

PDC Notes

You can move from the Bomb into moves such as the Pike or Hands Free Chopper or simply transition back into your Inverted Crucifix.

Your Notes

Bridged Handstand

Also known as:

Moon Handstand,

PDC Notes

Good flexibility required for this beautiful handstand variation.

Your Notes

Cartwheel Handspring Walkover

PDC Notes

Gymnastic skills required!
Master the handspring first
and make sure you can do a
non-pole based Cartwheel.

Your Notes

Caterpillar Pose

Also known as:
Inverted Pose, Reverse Climb Pose

PDC Notes
Once you have mastered this try the Caterpillar climb and Reverse Caterpillar too.

Your Notes

Caterpillar Pose (elbow grip)

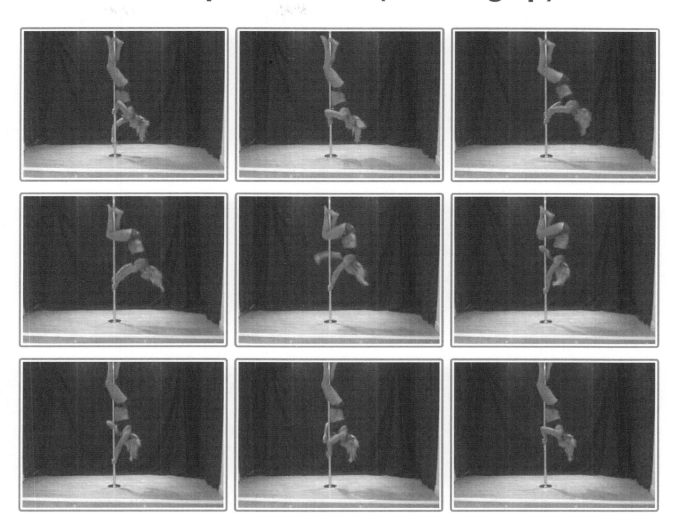

PDC Notes

This can be done with an elbow or forearm grip. Master this then try the Caterpillar Climb.

Your Notes

Caterpillar Pose (forearm grip)

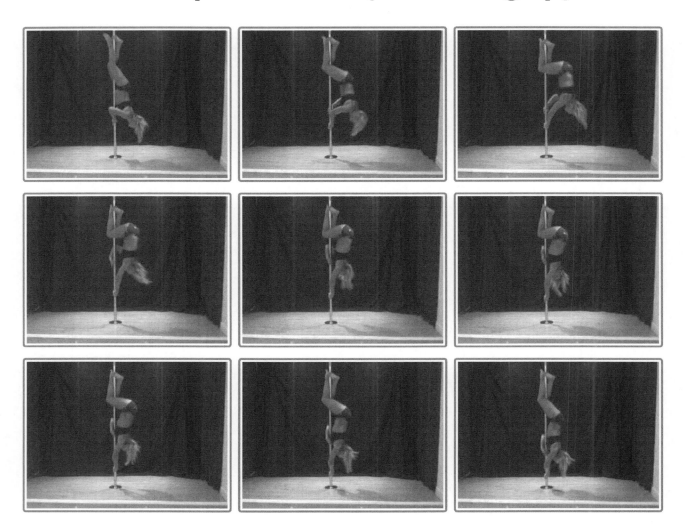

Also known as:

PDC Notes

This can be done with an elbow or forearm grip. Master this then try the Caterpillar Climb.

Your Notes

Chinese Pole Climb

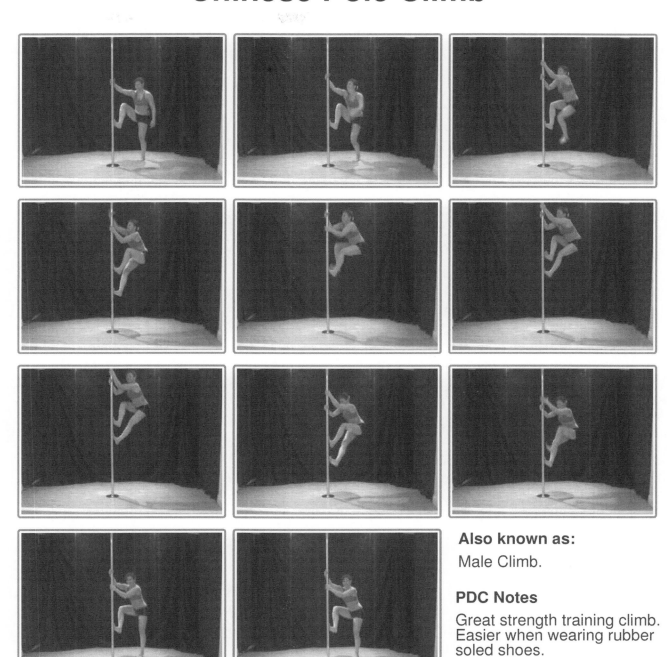

Also known as:

Male Climb.

PDC Notes

Great strength training climb. Easier when wearing rubber soled shoes.

Your Notes

Chopper

Also known as:

Over-V, Helicopter, Eagle

PDC Notes

Ensure legs are fully extended and toes are pointed. Master the Basic Invert and Inverted Crucifix first.

Your Notes

Combo 22

PDC Notes

A lovely fluid combination. You need to be able to Shoulder Mount with the Princess Grip and be able to do the Gemini (one-handed) to perfect this spinning combination.

Your Notes

Corkscrew Spin (no handed)

Also known as:

Helter Skelter Spin,

PDC Notes

Risk of serious bruising and abrasion to inner arm and armpit. Perfect the Corkscrew Spin (one handed) first.

Your Notes

Corkscrew Spin (one handed)

Also known as:

Helter Skelter Spin,

PDC Notes

Once you have mastered this spin you can try the Corkscrew (no handed). You can start the spin with either hand at the top.

PDC Notes

Cupid (closed)

Also known as:
Hummingbird, Bird,

PDC Notes
Perfect Ballet Hooks first.

Your Notes

Cupid Flatline

Also known as:

Marley Straight Leg, Marley Flatline, Flying Cupid

PDC Notes

Be aware of pressure to locked knee. Point toes and fully extend for perfect alignment.

Your Notes

Dangerous Brian

Also known as:

Dangerous George, No Handed Bow and Arrow, Leg Swan

PDC Notes

Pressure to upper foot, counter balance with lower leg. Progress to Dangerous Bridge.

Your Notes

Dart (closed)

Also known as:

Crucifix Forward Fold Variation.

PDC Notes

Ensure good horizontal lines by keeping the head low as shown.

Your Notes

Dart (open)

Also known as:

Crucifix Forward Fold Variation.

PDC Notes

Try the Dart (closed) variation first. Point your toes and fingers for maxium effect. Ensure good horizontal alignment through the legs and upper body.

Your Notes

Dove

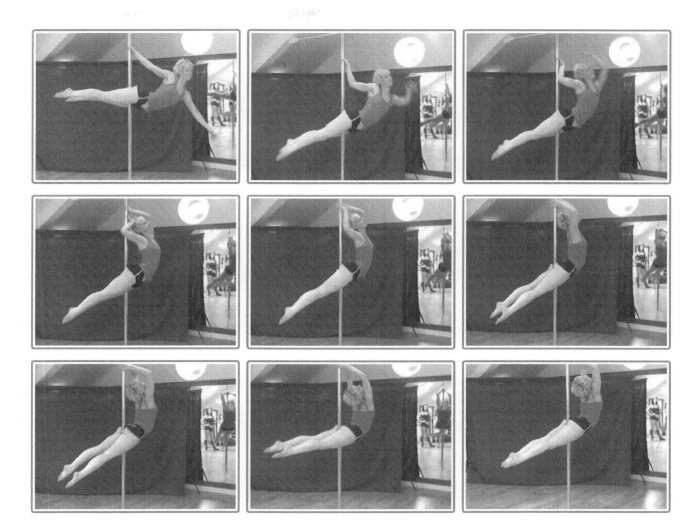

Also known as:

Half Crescent, Upright Bridge

PDC Notes

Good Lower back flexibility needed. Ideal progression from the Superman.

Your Notes

Embrace (one handed)

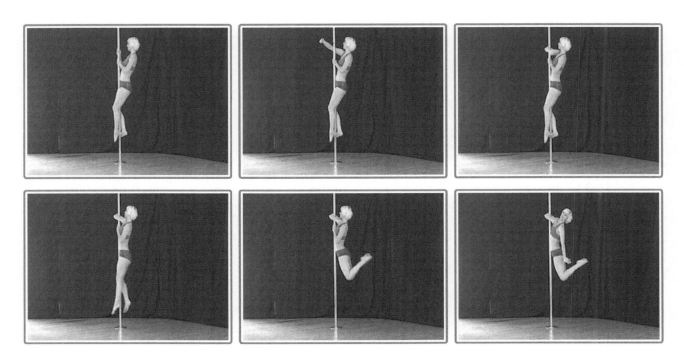

Also known as:

Elbow Hold Hangman.

PDC Notes

Master the Embrace (two handed) first. Point your toes and extend through the back for perfect alignment.

Your Notes

Emotion

Also known as:

Cradle Gemini, Recliner Gemini

PDC Notes

Master the Cradle first. Good flexibility required for this one.

Your Notes

Extended Butterfly

Also known as:

Papillon, Moth, Fiona

PDC Notes

Perfect Butterfly first. You can transition from the Butterfly, Apprentice or Parallel Handstand.

Your Notes

	Logo	Logo	Logo	Logo	Logo
Logo	PDC Registered Instructor	PDC Registered Instructor	PDC Approved Instructor	PDC Approved Instructor	PDC Pioneer Award
Title	Registered 1*	Registerd 2*	Approved 3*	Approved 4*	Pioneer
Pole Experience	Less than 2 years	Minimum of 2 years	Minimum of 3 years	Minimum of 3 years	Minimum of 5 years
Must Abide by Code of Conduct	✓	✓	✓	✓	✓
Produce Insurance Documents	✓	✓	✓	✓	✓
Provide Pole C.V.	✓	✓	✓	✓	✗
Subject to Random Studio Visit	✓	✓	✓	✓	✗
Pass PDC Approved Course	✓	✓	✓ Either	Evidence of ongoing career development	✗
Pass PDC Approved Grading	✓ AAP Level 3	✓ AAP Level 4	✓ Or AAP Level 4	✗	✗
Provide Member References	✗	✗	✗	✓	✗
Subject to Full Membership Vote	✗	✗	✗	✗	✓
Notes	New instructors, looking to start off doing things right	Instructors with just less than the three years required for full Approval	Full Approved status - our benchmark for excellence	Additional recognition for positive community involvement	Awarded for long-standing achievement

Figurehead (one handed)

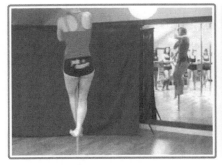 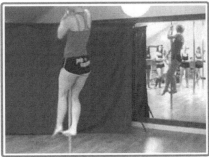 

 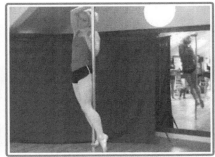 

Also known as:
Statue, Titanic, Crescent Moon.

PDC Notes
Perfect 2 handed variation first. Ideal transition from Side Climb.

Flying Yogini

Also known as:

Closed Rocket Man

PDC Notes

A nice variation on the traditional Yogini and a good prep for the Rocket Man.

Your Notes

Gemini (semi-closed)

Also known as:

Scorpio Variation, Inside Leg Hang Variation

PDC Notes

Progress to the Gemini (closed), Gemini Extreme and Gemini Kateriina.

Your Notes

Gemini Bridge

Also known as:

Bridged Scorpio, Inside Leg Hang Bridged, Overhead Gemini

PDC Notes

This is a beautiful Gemini Variation. Ensure good flexibility to improve the visual appeal of the move.

Your Notes

Gemini Handstand

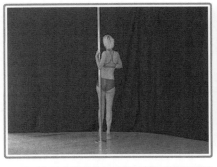  

Also known as:

Flatline Scorpio, Flatliner, Leg Over Lady, Sailboat

PDC Notes

Correct height is essential for correct execution - if you are too near the floor it won't work. Keep your inner shoulder blade resting against the pole.

Your Notes

Gemini Plank

Also known as:

Flatline Scorpio, Flatliner, Leg Over Lady, Sailboat

PDC Notes

Ensure good horizontal alignment.

Your Notes

Gemini Plank (from invert)

Also known as:

Gemini Flatliner

PDC Notes

Try also Gemini Plank from Extended Butterfly. Ensure good horizontal alignment.

Your Notes

Hands Free Chopper (closed)

Also known as:

Inverted Hip Hold, Star, Advanced Helicopter

PDC Notes

Try also the Hands Free Chopper (open) and then progress to Hands Free Chopper to Superman.

Your Notes

Hands Free Chopper (open)

Also known as:

Advanced Helicopter, Inverted Hip Hold, Star

PDC Notes

Ensure good skin contact on inner thigh. Point your toes!

Your Notes

Hang Glider (closed)

Also known as:

Hayley's Gemini

PDC Notes

Once you have perfected this try the Hang Glider (open).

Your Notes

Hang Glider (open)

Also known as:

Fallen Star variation

PDC Notes

Try also the closed version of this move and the Fallen Star.

Your Notes

Hangman

Also known as:

Shoulder Mount Prep

PDC Notes

Excellent strength training for triceps and abs.

Your Notes

Hummingbird

Also known as:

Cupid Leanout, Bird

PDC Notes

Master the Cupid first before trying this tricky variation.
Images show the move executed from a Side Climb.

Your Notes

Inverted Pike

Also known as:

Inverted Hip Hold, Inverted Pike

PDC Notes

Good Skin contact required on the upper,inner thighs. Try also the Chopper.

Your Notes

Knot

Also known as:

Recliner Variation

PDC Notes

Master the Cradle and Cradle Invert first.

Your Notes

Panteras Bow and Arrow

 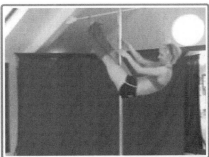 

Also known as:

Archer

PDC Notes

If you don't like this hand grip try the Extended Archer instead.

Your Notes

Panteras Gemini

Also known as:

Classic Gemini

PDC Notes

Pull the outside leg towards the head for full effect.

Your Notes

Pencil Pose

Also known as:

PDC Notes

There are several different grips you can use for this trick.

Your Notes

Post Spin

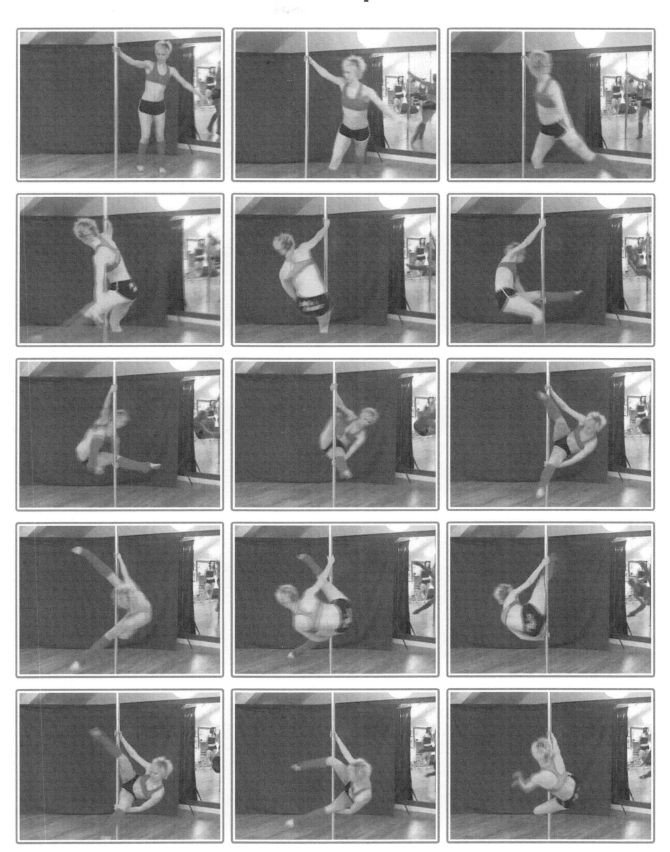

Also known as:

Thread Through Spin, Thread the Needle Spin, Legs Through Hands Spin, Donna Spin

PDC Notes

Tilt your head/upper body away from the pole like a Side Spin to help you get your knee through.

Your Notes

Recliner Invert

Also known as:

Recliner Invert

PDC Notes

Ensure you can invert first before attempting this. Be aware of pressure to lower thumb joint and outer forearm as well as rotation to outside shoulder.

Your Notes

Recliner Pike

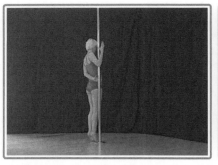  

Also known as:

Cradle Concorde, Back Support Concorde, Recliner Concorde

PDC Notes

Pressure to forearm of lower arm plus rotation to shoulder. Master the Recliner first.

Your Notes

Reiko Splits (one handed)

Also known as:

Chinese Star

PDC Notes

Strong work for your inside shoulder. Don't forget to point your toes on your outside foot. Try the two handed variation first.

Your Notes

Reverse Attitude Spin to Reverse Grab Spin

Also known as:

Showgirl Variation to Floater Transition

PDC Notes

Learn Black Widow Spin and Reverse Grab Spin first before attempting this dramatic combination.

Your Notes

Reverse Grab Spin

Also known as:
Flying Polecat, Coil Spin, Flying Spiral

PDC Notes
Excellent grip required on upper hand.

Your Notes

Reverse Grab Spin to Back Hook Spin

Also known as:

Coil Spin to Dizzy Spin, Flying Spiral Spin to Back Hook Spin,

PDC Notes

Master the Reverse Grab Spin and Back Hook Spin individually before trying this lovely combination.

Your Notes

Reverse Grab Spin to Chair Spin

Also known as:

Reverse Grab Spin to Carousel Spin, Flying Polecat Spin to Carousel Spin, Coil Spin to Carousel Spin, Flying Spiral Spin to Chair Spin

PDC Notes

Master the Reverse Grab Spin and Chair Spin individually before trying this lovely combination.

Your Notes

Reverse Grab to Reverse Attitude Spin

Also known as:

Reverse Grab to Reverse Attitude Spin, Flying Polecat Spin to Black Widow Spin, Coil Spin to Reverse Attitude Spin, Flying Spiral Spin to Reverse Attitude Spin

PDC Notes

Lots of momentum required.

Your Notes

Rocket Man (closed)

Also known as:

PDC Notes

Once you have mastered this try the Rocket Man (open). Good skin contact needed on abdomen and under arm.

Your Notes

Seated Climb

 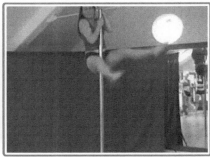 

Also known as:

PDC Notes

Good upper body strength required.

Your Notes

Seated Descent

Also known as:

Your Notes

Seated Jack Knife

Also known as:

Seated Pointer, Thigh Conditioner

PDC Notes

Tough on the inner thighs but a nice conditioning move. Ensure you are comfortable in the no handed Seat variations first.

Your Notes

Shooting Star

Also known as:

Bottom Handed Viva

PDC Notes

Excellent prep for the Tea Pot.

Your Notes

Shoulder Dismount (bow and arrow legs)

Also known as:

Reverse Shoulder Mount

PDC Notes

Master the V-legs or prayer legs first. Ensure you are strong in both the triceps and abs.

Your Notes

Shoulder Dismount (prayer legs)

Also known as:

PDC Notes

This is a great way to work towards Shoulder Mounts and is excellent for the abs and triceps.

Your Notes

Shoulder Mount

  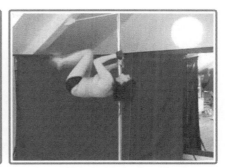

Also known as:

Super Invert

PDC Notes

Master Shoulder Dismount first.

Your Notes

Shoulder Mount Straddle

Also known as:

Shoulder Mount V-legs, Shoulder Mount Boomerang

PDC Notes

Master the Shoulder Mount first.

Your Notes

Shoulder Mount Tuck

Also known as:

PDC Notes

Master the Shoulder Mount first. Progress to Shoulder Mount Pencil.

Your Notes

Side Climb

Also known as:

PDC Notes

Bruising likely for back of knee and climbing foot when learning.

Your Notes

Side Spin to Superman

Also known as:

JK Spin

PDC Notes

More painful than the Superman so condition to the classic Superman first

Your Notes

Skater (elbow hold)

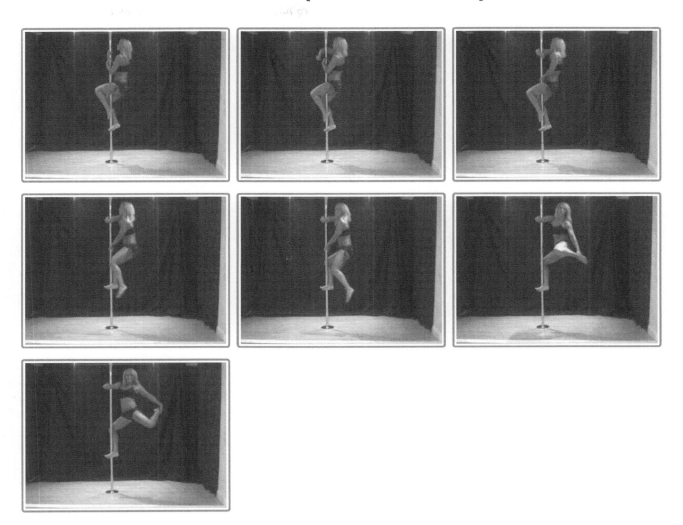

Also known as:

PDC Notes

Try also the Skater (forearm grip) and progress to the Chinese Skater.

Your Notes

Skater (forearm grip)

Also known as:

PDC Notes

Try the Skater (elbow hold) and progress to the Chinese Skater.

Your Notes

Snake Spin

Also known as:

PDC Notes

Beautiful combination spin. Master the Black Widow Spin first.

Your Notes

Spinning Chopper

Also known as:

Spinning Helicopter

PDC Notes

Master the Chopper first. Ensure excellent hand grip particularly on your upper hand.

Your Notes

Spinning Climb

Also known as:

Spinning Climb

PDC Notes

Master the Monkey Climb first. Great move for strengthening the upper body.

Your Notes

Spinning Superman

Also known as:

Spinning Supergirl

PDC Notes

Try also the Side Spin to Superman.

Your Notes

Split Heel Pose (one handed)

Also known as:

PDC Notes

Good Flexibility required. Be aware of pressure to the knees.

Your Notes

Split Straddle

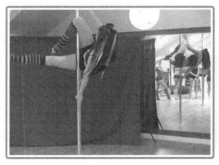 

Also known as:

Jamilla Variation

PDC Notes

Be aware of pressure to the lower forearm.

Your Notes

Stag

Also known as:

Twisted Yogini

PDC Notes

Good flexibility will allow you to execute this move beautifully.

Your Notes

Stargazer

Also known as:

PDC Notes

Risk of pressure to lower back.

Your Notes

Straddle Spin (one handed)

Also known as:

Straddle Spin, Anchor Spin,

PDC Notes

Master Boomerang Spin (two handed) first. Excellent grip required.

Your Notes

Superman

Also known as:

PDC Notes

This will be painful to learn, lots of burn to the inner thigh.

Your Notes

Swan Dive

Also known as:

PDC Notes

Risk of pressure to lower back.

Your Notes

Tail Drop

Also known as:

Handstand Drop

PDC Notes

Good flexibility will help with perfect execution. Point your toes throughout.

Your Notes

Tail Drop to Splits

Also known as:

Classic Tail Drop.

PDC Notes

Good flexibility will help you execute this move perfectly. As you slide down the pole move the pelvis slightly off centre to avoid unecessary abrasion in unwanted areas.

Your Notes

Tail Pipe

Also known as:

PDC Notes

Good hamstring flexibility required.

Your Notes

Tail Sit

Also known as:

Spider, Tail Pipe

PDC Notes

Srong upper back strength needed.

Your Notes

Tea Pot

Also known as:

PDC Notes

Master the Mantis or Shooting Star first. Slightly arching the lower back and pushing the pelvis forwards helps perfect execution.

Your Notes

Teddy

Also known as:

PDC Notes

Good skin contact required on the under arm - expect to experience discomfort when learning.

Your Notes

True Tammy

Also known as:

Goddess, Outside Knee Hang

PDC Notes

Be aware of pressure to the calf muscle when learning.

Your Notes

Turtle Dove

Also known as:

Diagonal Dove.

PDC Notes

This is an easier version of the dove that requires less back flexibility.

Your Notes

Turtle Dove (one handed)

Also known as:
Figurehead, Diagonal Statue

PDC Notes
Be aware of pressure to your lower back when transitioning into this move.

Your Notes

Twisted Wrist Sit (bracket grip)

Also known as:

Ladygarden, V-Seat, Daphne, Plank variation, Advanced Layback

PDC Notes

Good thigh contact is essential, be aware of pressure to lower back and hyper-extension of elbow. Can be executed with the bottom hand facing up or down - see Advanced Layback (half bracket grip).

Your Notes

Twisted Wrist Sit (half bracket grip)

Also known as:

Ladygarden, V-Seat, Daphne, Plank variation, Advanced Layback

PDC Notes

Good thigh contact is essential, be aware of pressure to lower back and hyper extension of elbow. Can be executed with the bottom hand facing up or down - see Advanced Layback (bracket grip).

Your Notes

Western Flag

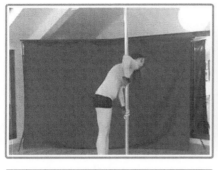  

Also known as:

Flag

PDC Notes

Good core strength required and you will need skin contact on your upper, inner arm.

Your Notes

Western Flag (one handed knee to pole)

Also known as:

Flag variation.

PDC Notes

Master the Western Flag first.

Your Notes

Western Flag Invert (from floor)

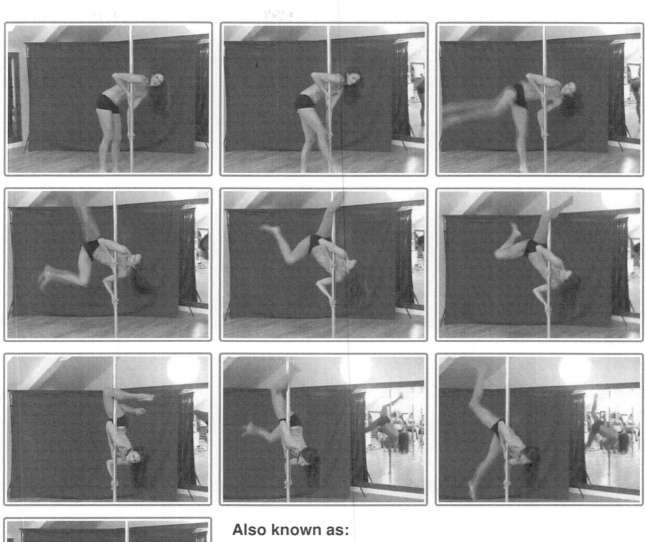

Also known as:

Flag Invert.

PDC Notes

Master the Western Flag first.

Your Notes

Western Flag Matrix

Also known as:

Flag Attitude

PDC Notes

A pretty alternative to the traditional Western Flag.

Your Notes

Windscreen Wiper

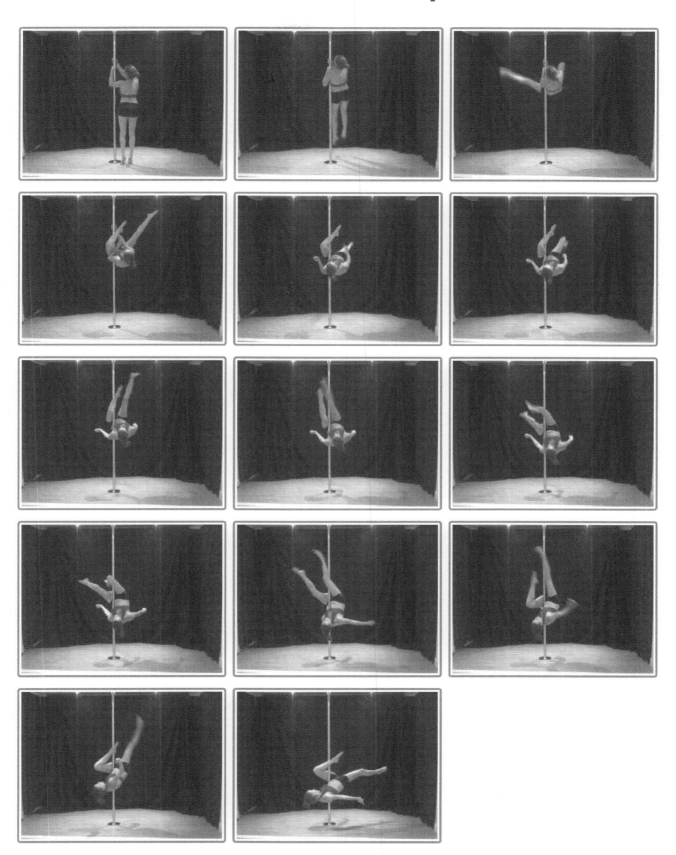

Also known as:

Static Electic Leg Switch.

PDC Notes

Good prep for Electric Leg Switch.

Your Notes

263

Yogi Handstand

Also known as:

PDC Notes
Be aware of pressure to the lower wrist and hand.

Your Notes

Yogi Lift

Also known as:

PDC Notes
This is a great way to start an Aerial Climb.

Yogini

Also known as:

PDC Notes

Be aware of pressure to the lower back. Good skin contact required on abdomen and under arm.

Your Notes

Yogini Lily

Also known as:

PDC Notes

Great preparation for Yogini.

Your Notes

Level 5

Aerial Climb

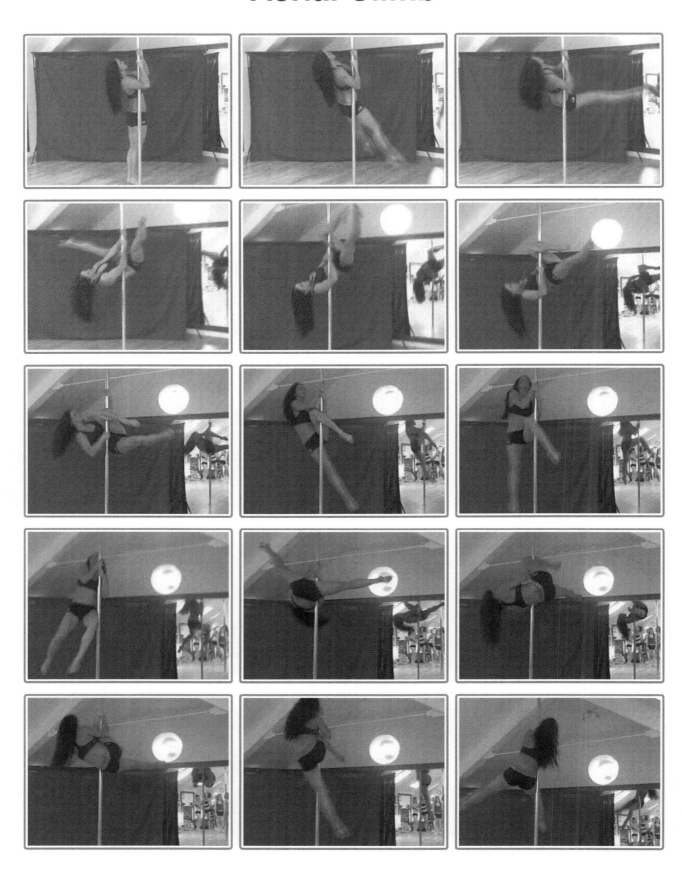

Also known as:
Tissu Climb, Silk Climb, Double Climb, Knee Climb

PDC Notes
Bruising likely on back of knee when learning. Excellent strength required.

Your Notes

Air Recliner Invert

Also known as:

Air Recliner Invert, Super Recliner, Back Support Invert

PDC Notes

Extreme pressure to forearm on inside arm plus rotation to outside shoulder. Master the move from the floor before trying the air variation.

Your Notes

Air Shoulder Mount

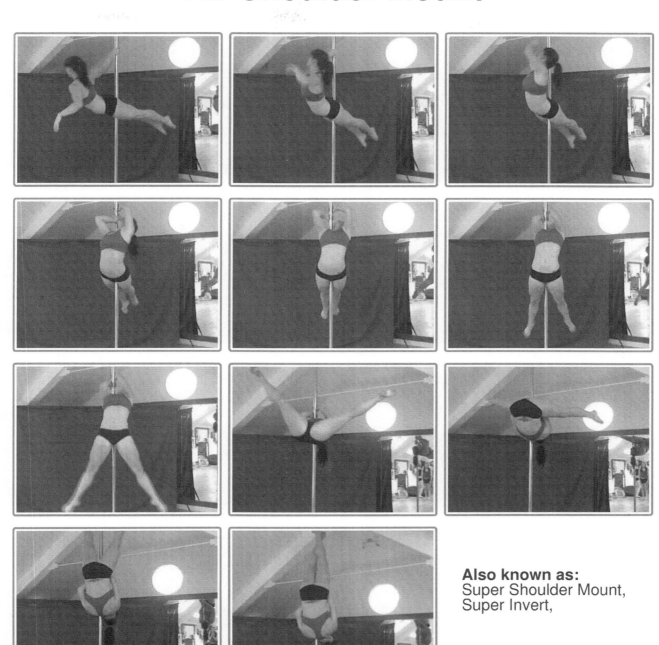

Also known as:
Super Shoulder Mount,
Super Invert,

PDC Notes
Master normal Shoulder Mount first or build up strength using Shoulder Dismounts.
Skin contact recommended on shoulder.

Your Notes

Air Walk (bracket grip)

Also known as:

Jenyne Walk

PDC Notes

Mime walking movement. Extreme pressure to lower forearm/wrist.

Your Notes

Air Walk (forearm grip)

Also known as:

Jenyne Walk.

PDC Notes

Slow down the walk for dramatic effect and point the toes. Be aware of pressure to the lower wrist.

Your Notes

Allegra (closed)

Also known as:

PDC Notes

Good back flexibility required. Ideal transition from Gemini Plank.

Your Notes

Allegra (open)

Also known as:

PDC Notes

Good back flexibility required. Ideal transition from Gemini Plank

Your Notes

Arms Only Climb

  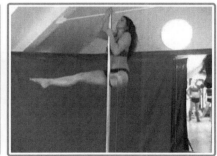

Also known as:

Super Climb, No Legs Climb

PDC Notes

Extreme upper body strength required. Master the
Seated Climb first.

Your Notes

Ayesha (forearm grip)

Also known as:

Forearm hold handstand

PDC Notes

Pressure to lower and upper forearm. You may prefer the Ayesha (elbow grip).
Progress to Straight Edge.

Your Notes

Back Hook to Shoulder Mount

Also known as:

Dizzy Spin to Shoulder Mount.

PDC Notes

Master the Back Hook Spin and Shoulder Mount separatley ensuring you are comfortable with doing your Shoulder Mount with the princess grip.

Your Notes

Banana Splits

Also known as:

Downward Facing Splits. Inverted Pole Splits.

PDC Notes

Flexibility and strength involved.

Your Notes

Brass Bridge

Also known as:

Extended Scorpio, Bridged Eros.

PDC Notes

Nice progression from Brass Monkey. Strong knee contact required.

Your Notes

Brass Monkey Ascent to Pole Sit

Also known as:

PDC Notes

Good skin contact required on back of inner knee.

Your Notes

Bridge

Also known as:

PDC Notes

Master the Bat first and ensure you have good back flexibility.

Your Notes

Butterfly (one handed)

 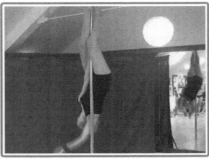 

Also known as:

1 handed Papillion, 1 handed Moth, 1 handed Lotus, 1 handed Venus.

PDC Notes

Ideal progression from Butterfly. Strong grip required on lower hand and upper calf.

Your Notes

Caterpillar Climb

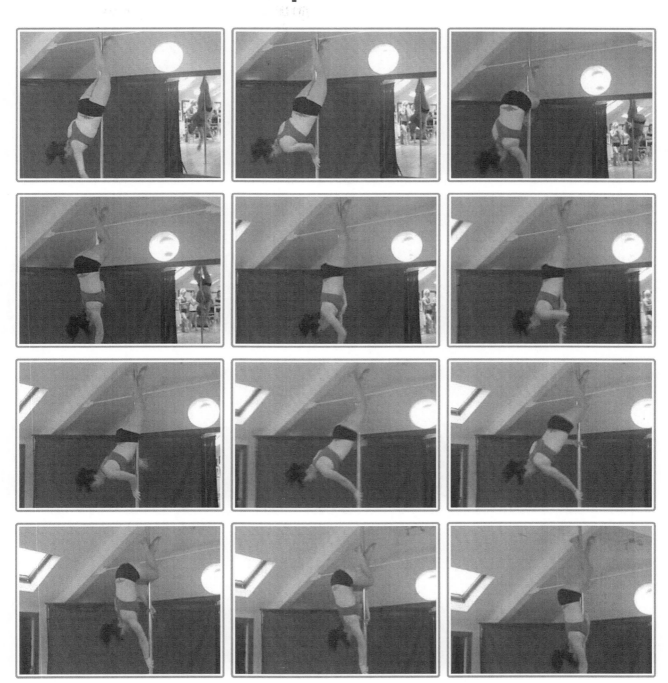

Also known as:

Reverse Climb, Inverted Climb,

PDC Notes

Work on Cat Pose and Reverse Caterpillar too.

Your Notes

Caterpillar Descent

Also known as:
Reverse Caterpillar Climb

PDC Notes

Your Notes

Chinese Skater

Also known as:

Reiko Split Variation.

PDC Notes

Excellent strength and flexiblility required to execute this move well.

Your Notes

Crescent

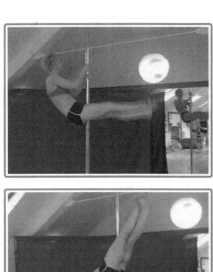

Also known as:

Pantera's Moon.

PDC Notes

Be aware of pressure to lower back.

Your Notes

Cupid to Reverse Shoulder Mount

Also known as:

Hummingbird or Bird to Shoulder Dismount,

PDC Notes

Master the Cupid and Shoulder Dismount individually first.

Your Notes

Cupid to Twisted Grip Ayesha

Also known as:
Hummingbird or Bird to Twisted Grip Ayesha.

PDC Notes

Master the Cupid and Twisted Grip Ayesha individually before trying this advanced trick combination.

Your Notes

Deadlift Handstand (into pole)

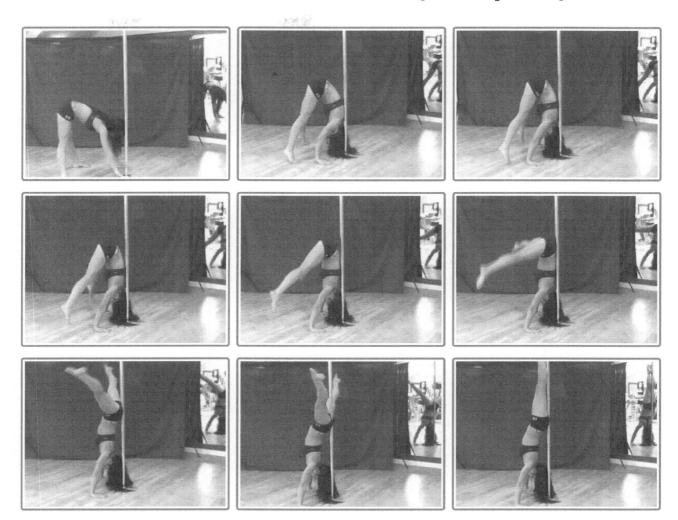

Also known as:

Elephant Lift

PDC Notes

Move hands away rom pole to allow you to lean into the pole, then you can lock the abs, push up onto the toes and lift.

Your Notes

Double Knees

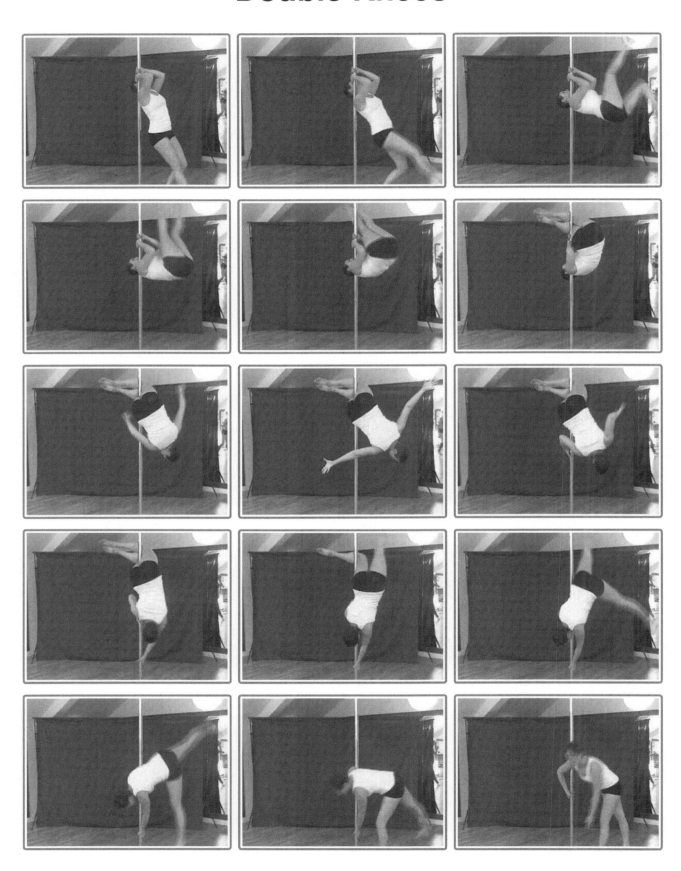

Also known as:

Twisted Knees

PDC Notes

Ensure excellent grip on back of knees and good core strength.

Your Notes

Elbow Iron X

Also known as:

PDC Notes

Excellent core strength required, don't forget to point the toes.

Your Notes

Electric Leg Switch

Also known as:

Electric KT

PDC Notes

Your Notes

Embrace Extreme

Also known as:

Elbow Hold Hangman.

PDC Notes

For full Embrace Extreme lift back leg up to increase the back arch and create more visual impact.

Your Notes

Epose

Also known as:

Deadlift Prep.

PDC Notes

Good core and upper body strength required.

Your Notes

Fallen Star

Also known as:

Aries, Back-split, Marksman, Free Glider, Minx, Overhead, Inverted V

PDC Notes

Progress to Side Bow and Arrow.

Your Notes

Felix Figurehead

Also known as:

Bees Knees

PDC Notes

Good back flexibility required. Ideal transition from the Superman.

Your Notes

Floating Ballerina

Also known as:

Twisted Stag

PDC Notes

You will need good spinal flexibility to get into this move. Watch for pressure to the ribs when learning.

Your Notes

Floorsweeper Spin

Also known as:

PDC Notes

Extreme shoulder rotation involved.

Your Notes

Full Moon

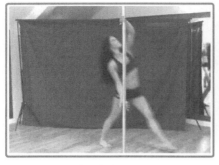  

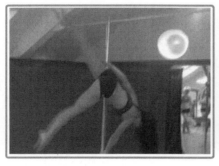  

Also known as:

Parralel Handstand Flip

PDC Notes

Use a cup grip and ensure you are competent with moves such as the Parallel Handstand before trying this. Work on the Half Moon first.

Your Notes

Funky Monkey

Also known as:

Extreme Brass Monkey, Brass Monkey (closed)

PDC Notes

Ensure your toes are pointed and you have excellent skin contact on the back of the calf muscle and knee.

Your Notes

Gemini (closed)

Also known as:

Scorpio (closed), Inside Leg Hang Extended.

PDC Notes

Good Flexibility required. Master more basic Gemini variations before trying this one.

Your Notes

Gemini (one handed) to Twisted Grip Ayesha

Also known as:

Scorpio (one handed) to Twisted Grip Ayesha

PDC Notes

Advanced trick combination. Master Gemini (one handed) and Twisted Grip Ayesha in isolation before attempting this combination.

Your Notes

Gemini Extreme

Also known as:

Scorpio Extreme

PDC Notes

Excellent flexibility required. Master the Gemini first.

Your Notes

Gemini Kateriina

Also known as:

Scorpio Kateriina, Inside Leg Hang Variation

PDC Notes

This move will apply pressure to the ribs and back so attempt with caution. Try also the Allegra (closed).

Your Notes

Gemini Plank (from Butterfly)

Also known as:

Flatline (from Butterfly)

PDC Notes

Your Notes

313

Gemini Plank (from Extended Butterfly)

Also known as:

Gemini Flatliner

PDC Notes

Your Notes

Instructor Training Courses

We are pleased to recommend PDC Approved Teacher Training Courses.
These member-run courses have each undergone a rigerous approval process to ensure that they provide you with quality carreer progression as well as value for money.
Please refer to the website for current course details and availability.

Funky Monkey Studio Pole Instructor Training Program.
This course offers an in-depth look at how to become a safe pole dancing instructor and requires that you have previous pole dancing experience.

The Pole Studio Instructor Training Programme.
Through successful completion of this PDC Approved course you will gain an internationally recognised qualification in pole dance fitness instruction for beginner level. The skills and teaching methods you develop during the instructor training programme are transferable skills that can be applied to all levels of pole dance fitness teaching.

Spin City Pole Fitness Teacher Training.
Spin City Pole Fitness Teacher Training is a PDC Approved Training Course. Training is available at beginners level with options to continue with your professional development via 1 day workshops.

Empowerment Through Dance Ltd. Pole Dancing Instructor Certification Programs
This is a full "certification" course - so you will be certified to teach pole dancing sanctioned by nationally recognized pole dance organizations who know the pole dancing business. You will receive a certification, not a certificate of completion.

Discoveries Dance Pole Dance Training Program
Professional, scientific and designed by a certified educator who has been teaching since 2007.
This pole dance training program was developed to provide professional guidance and quality education for both budding and seasoned pole instructors. This course is designed to assist the experienced pole enthusiast in developing her teaching and safety skills.

Vertical Dance Pole Instructor Program
The Vertical Dance Pole Instructor Program has been created for every one who wishes to teach pole fitness. Whether you have little or no skill, or you have been teaching pole fitness for years. The course is suitable for those with or without fitness or dance certifications and the beginner level has no prerequisite in order to sign up.

Gripper

 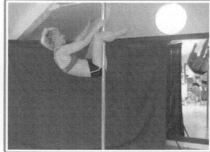 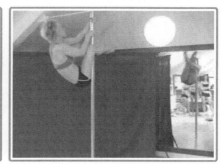

Also known as:

Foot hold sit-up

PDC Notes

Ensure good contact between the top foot and the pole.

Your Notes

Half Moon

Also known as:

Handstand Flip

PDC Notes

Use a cup grip and ensure you are competent with moves such as the Parallel Handstand before trying this. Once you have mastered this try the Full Moon.

Your Notes

Holly Drop

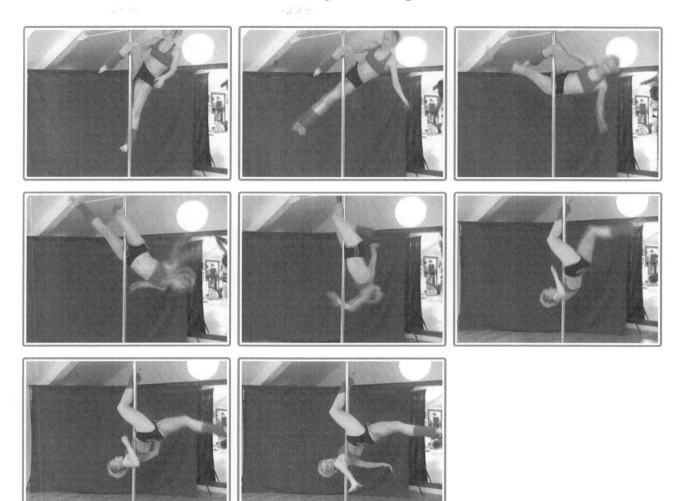

Also known as:

Cupid Drop

PDC Notes

Ensure you have mastered the Gemini before learning this stunning combination.

Your Notes

Iguana Mount (pencil split)

Also known as:

Jewel, Hands Free Handstand, Fang, Iguana V

PDC Notes

Good hand grip required. Master the Floor Inversion and/or Headstand Sit-up first. Also try Iguana (prayer legs).

Your Notes

Iguana Mount (prayer pose)

Also known as:

Jewel, Hands Free
Handstand, Fang

PDC Notes

Good hand grip required. Master the Floor Inversion and/or
Headstand Sit-up first. Also try Iguana (pencil) and Iguana
(pencil split).

Your Notes

Inverted D

Also known as:

Wingless Moth

PDC Notes

Master the Extended Butterfly first.

Your Notes

Iron X

Also known as:

X-Man

PDC Notes

Excellent core strength and flexibility required.
Progress to Chinese Flag.

Your Notes

Jack Knife

Also known as:

PDC Notes

Can use classic or twisted grip.

Your Notes

Jade

Also known as:
Horizontal Splits on pole

PDC Notes

Make sure you can do the splits. Try to avoid placing your spare hand on your bottom.

Your Notes

Jamilla

Also known as:

Peanut

PDC Notes

Master the Apprentice first.

Your Notes

Jeanie

Also known as:

PDC Notes
Ensure the back of your knees are conditioned.
You will need great core strength.

Your Notes

Knees (closed)

 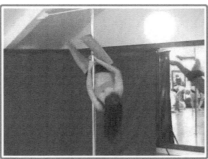 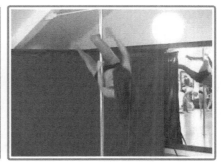

  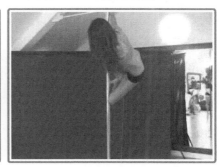

Also known as:

Knee Conditioning

PDC Notes

Be aware of extreme pressure to the knees!
Excellent core strength required.

Your Notes

Knees (open)

Also known as:

Knee Conditioning

PDC Notes

Be aware of extreme pressure to the knees! Excellent core strength required.

Your Notes

Matrix (bow and arrow legs)

 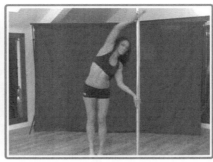 

Also known as:

Deadlift Pose

PDC Notes

Great way of boosting your strength. Looks amazing on a spinning pole. Progress to Matrix Walk.

> **Your Notes**

Noodle

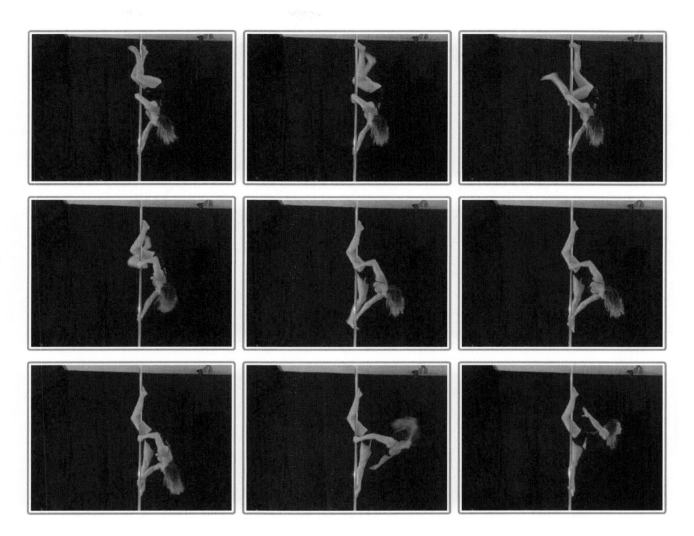

Also known as:

PDC Notes

Be aware of the extreme rotation on the upper ankle.

Your Notes

Parallel Handstand

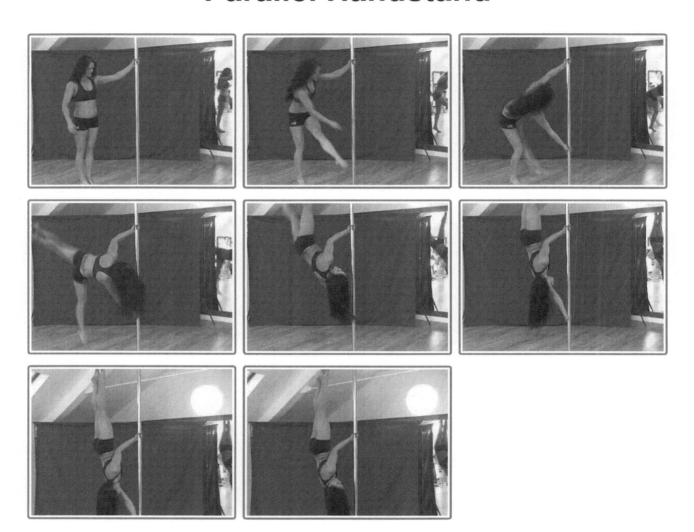

Also known as:

Split Grip straight Edge, Bracket Grip Straight Edge, Brace Grip Straight Edge

PDC Notes

Master the Basic Handspring first and then find the balance point where the pelivs is directly above the head. Ensure good vertical alignment.

Your Notes

Pendulum (cup grip)

Also known as:

PDC Notes

Excellent core and upper body strength required. Master Parallel and Twisted Grip Handstands first.

Your Notes

Phoenix

Also known as:

Reverse Grab Spin to Twisted Grip Deadlift

PDC Notes

Lots of momentum required as well as excellent upper body and core strength.

Your Notes

Poisson

Also known as:

Fish

PDC Notes

Arch the back for maximum visual effect. Images show the Poisson executed from a Basic Invert.

Your Notes

Also known as:

PDC Notes

Excellent contact required on back of knee, calf muscle and gluteal crease.

Your Notes

Remi

Also known as:

Remi Martin, Chinese Fall Back,

PDC Notes

Be aware of knee, quad and back pressure. If you are flexible try the Remi Extreme.

Your Notes

Remi Extreme

Also known as:
Chinese Pole Sit Back Bend, Chinese Fall Back,

PDC Notes
Excellent back flexibility required.

Your Notes

Reverse Poisson

Also known as:

PDC Notes

Try the Poisson first. Be aware that this moves requires a strong spinal twist.

Your Notes

Shoulder Dismount Plank (open)

Also known as:

Reverse Shoulder Mount Plank

PDC Notes

Excellent core strength required. Perfect other Shoulder Dismounts such as Straddle first.

Your Notes

Shoulder Mount Bounce Descent

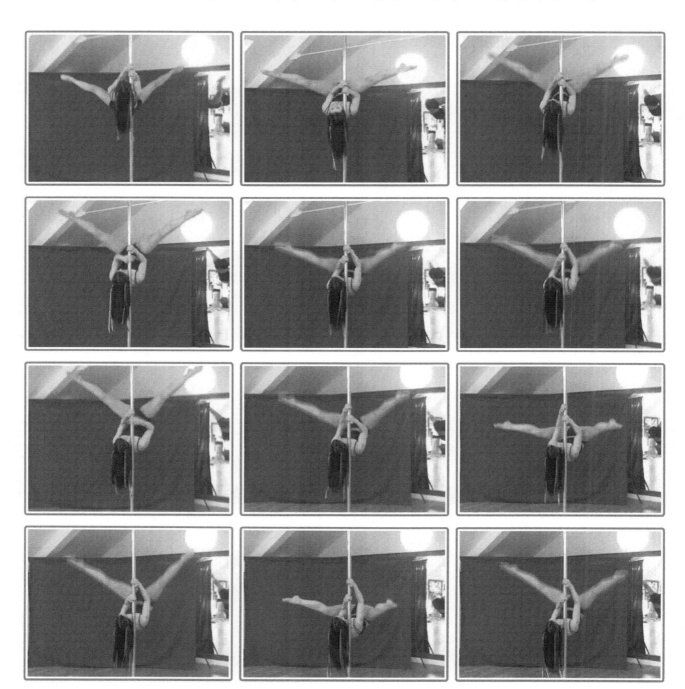

Also known as:

PDC Notes
Master the Shoulder Mount V-legs first.

Your Notes

Shoulder Mount Bounce Descent
(variation)

Also known as:

PDC Notes

Master the Shoulder
Mount V-legs first.

Your Notes

Shoulder Mount Flip

Also known as:

PDC Notes

Once you have mastered this try the Shoulder Mount to Seat.

Your Notes

Shoulder Mount Flip from Floor

Also known as:
Floor Shoulder Mount to Standing, Val D'Isere

PDC Notes
Master less advanced Shoulder Mount variations first.

Your Notes

Shoulder Mount Jack Knife

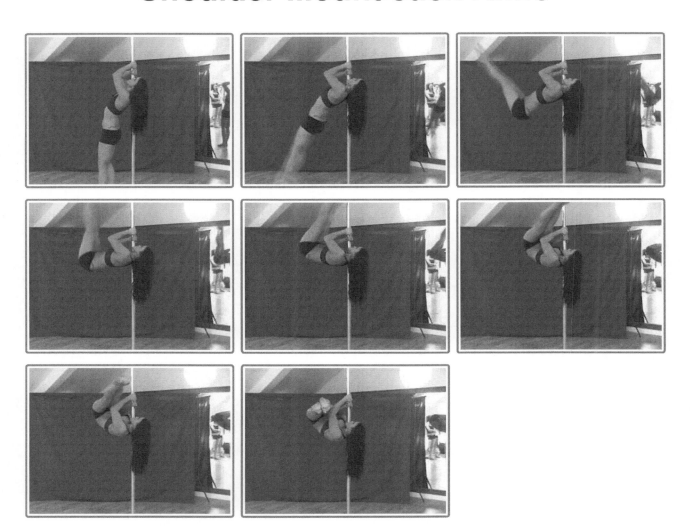

Also known as:

PDC Notes

Master the Shoulder Mount first and then work towards Shoulder Mount Flip.

Your Notes

Shoulder Mount Lock (one handed)

Also known as:

PDC Notes

Good skin contact needed on Shoulder.

Your Notes

Shoulder Mount Pencil

Also known as:

Superhold, Super Invert

PDC Notes

Master the Shoulder Mount and Shoulder Mount Tuck first.

Your Notes

347

Shoulder Mount Pop

Also known as:

PDC Notes

Ensure you are high enough up the pole when first attempting. You need to have perfected other Shoulder Mount techniques before trying this one.

Your Notes

Shoulder Mount Splits

  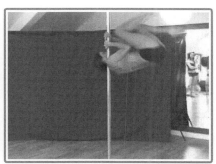

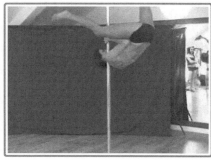 

Also known as:

PDC Notes

Good Split flexibility required for perfect execution.

Your Notes

Shoulder Mount to Seat

Also known as:

PDC Notes
Risk of bruising and abrasion to the shoulder. Master the Shoulder Mount Flip first.

Your Notes

Side Bow and Arrow

Also known as:

Fallen Star Drop

PDC Notes

Try also the Fallen Star.

Your Notes

Spin and Snap

Also known as:

PDC Notes

Master the One Handed Handstand first.

Your Notes

Spinning Shoulder Mount

 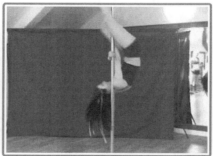 

Also known as:

Dislocater

PDC Notes

Spinning Shoulder Mounts can be executed with a number of different grips.

Your Notes

Split Heel Box Splits

Also known as:

PDC Notes

Excellent hip/leg flexibility required. Be aware of pressure to your inner knees.

Your Notes

Spyda Monkey

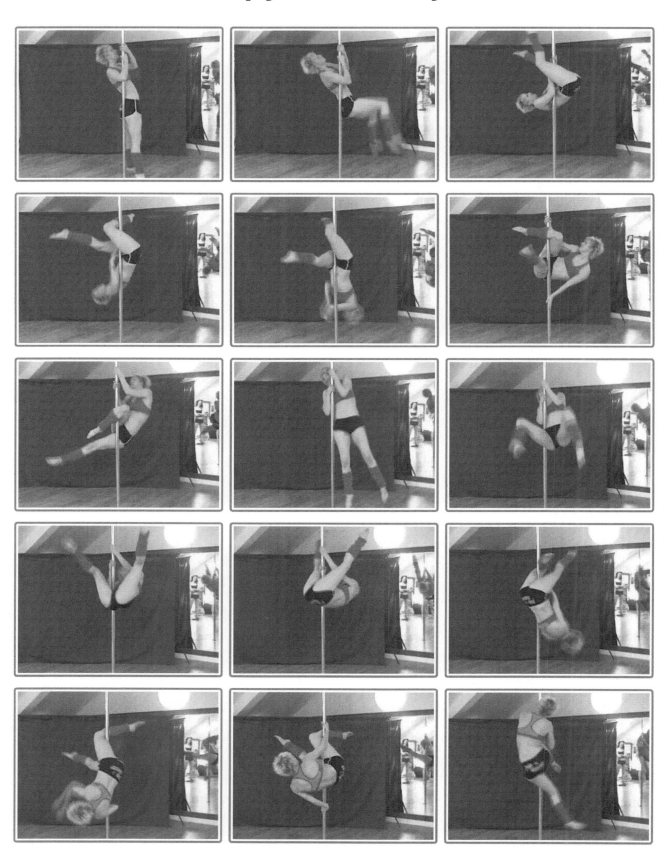

Also known as:

Gemini repeater

PDC Notes

Excellent upper body strength needed.

Your Notes

Straight Edge (elbow grip)

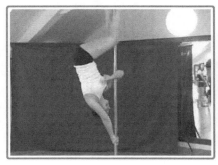  

Also known as:

PDC Notes

Excellent skin contact required on upper elbow and good grip on lower hand.

Your Notes

Straight Edge (forearm grip)

Also known as:

PDC Notes

Excellent skin contact required on upper forearm/hand and good grip on lower hand.

Your Notes

Suicide Back Hook Spin

Also known as:

Reverse Electric Leg Switch

PDC Notes

Ensure you have mastered inverts such as the Gemini and Windscreen Wiper before attempting this spin.

Your Notes

Super Sliding Splits

Also known as:

PDC Notes

Master the splits before attempting this move.

Your Notes

Swivel Hips

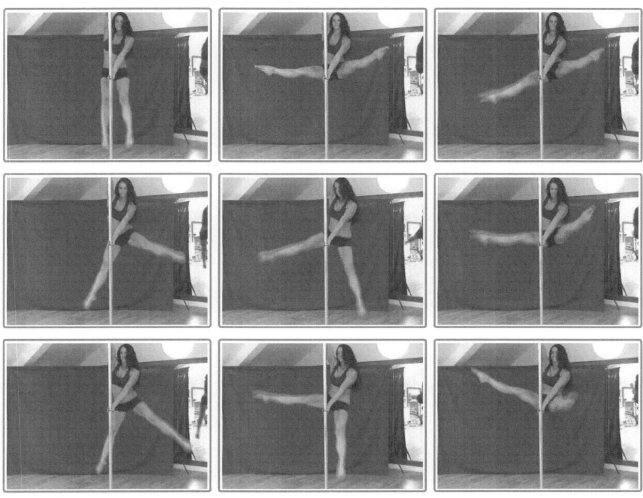

Also known as:

Boomerang Leg Circles, Rotating Carousel

PDC Notes

Lots of pressure on bottom wrist, excellent upper body and core strength required.

Your Notes

Tabletop

Also known as:

PDC Notes

Your Notes

Tail Drop to Straddle

Also known as:

Tail Drop to Cantilever, Bum Slide to V-Legs

PDC Notes

Your Notes

Tail Sit (one handed)

Also known as:

Spider (one handed), Tail Pipe

PDC Notes

Master the Spider first.

Your Notes

Teddy Pike

Also known as:

Teddy Variation

PDC Notes

Requires more strength and flexibility than the classic Teddy.

Your Notes

Tick Tock

Also known as:
Shoulder Mount Jack Knife repeaters.

PDC Notes
Master the Shoulder Mount first and progress to Shoulder Mount Circle.

Your Notes

Toothbrush

Also known as:

Chinese Pole Hold, Twisted Tabletop

PDC Notes

Good core strength involved. Ensure good horizontal alignment.

Your Notes

Tornado Roll

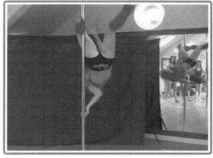  

Also known as:

PDC Notes

Ensure you are confident with moves such as the Eros, Eros Monkey and BrassMonkey before attempting this roll. You will need excellent grip on your inner knee.

Your Notes

Twisted Bow and Arrow

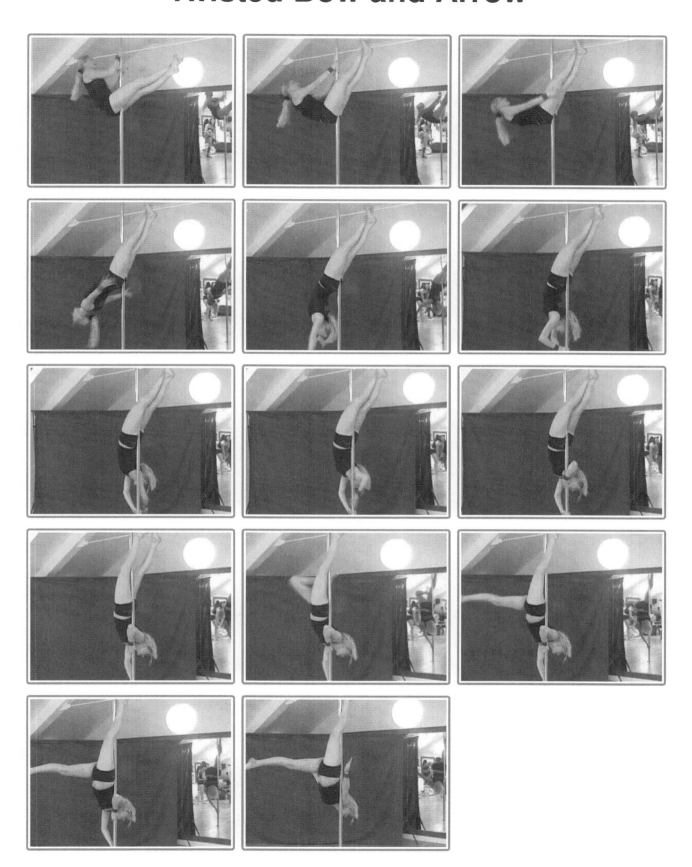

Also known as:

PDC Notes

Strong contact required on the under arm. Skin contact also required through the side of the body.

Your Notes

Twisted Grip Ayesha to Matrix

Also known as:

Twisted grip to Bow and arrow legs.

PDC Notes

Master the Twisted Grip Tuck first and then progress through the Twisted Grip variations.

Your Notes

Twisted Grip Deadlift

Also known as:

Phoenix Preparation

PDC Notes

Ideal progression from handspring. Excellent core strength required. Use moves such as Reverse Attitude Spin (bracket grip), Handspring Dart and Iron X to develop strength.

Your Notes

Twisted Grip Handstand (Prayer legs)

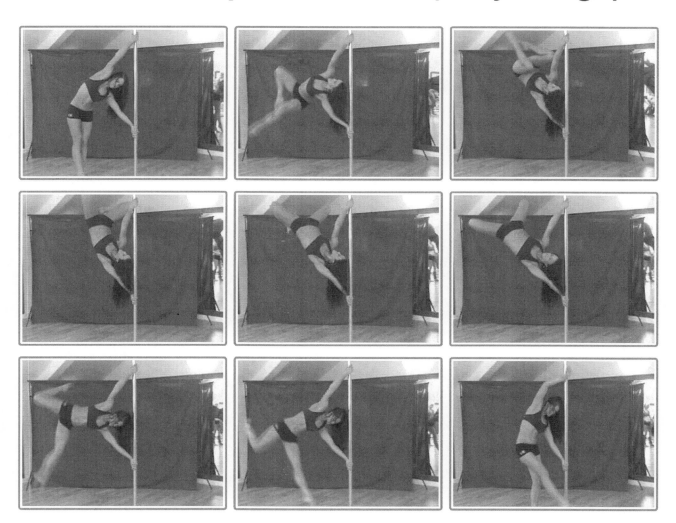

Also known as:

PDC Notes

Great upper body strength and balance required for perfect execution.

Your Notes

Twisted Grip Handstand to Iguana (pencil)

Also known as:

PDC Notes

Ensure excellent hand grip and that you have mastered the Twisted Grip and Iguana individually before attempting this advanced combination.

Your Notes

Twisted Grip Hangman

Also known as:

PDC Notes

Excellent core and upper body strength required.

Your Notes

Twisted Grip Horizontal Splits (open)

Also known as:

Twisted Grip Splits

PDC Notes

Good strength and flexibility required for the lovely twisted grip variation.

Your Notes

Twisted Grip Pose (one handed one leg bent one leg straight)

Also known as:

PDC Notes

Master the two handed Twisted Grip variations and Chopper first and ensure excellentgrip on upper arm.

Your Notes

Twisted Grip Tuck

Also known as:

PDC Notes

Good way to learn the Twisted Grip Handstand variations as you can master the balance point of the pelvis above the head.

Your Notes

Twisted Star

Also known as:

PDC Notes

Good back flexibility required and lots of skin contact around the abdomen and inner arm needed.

Your Notes

U-bend

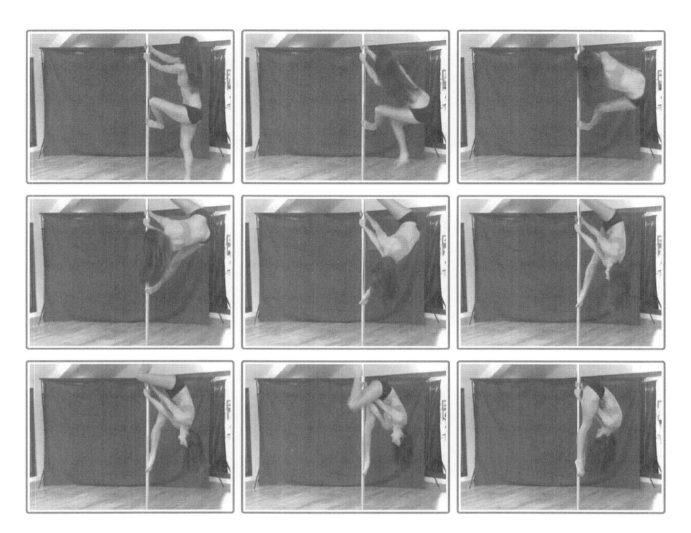

Also known as:

PDC Notes

Ensure excellent hand grip. Point the toes throughout.

Your Notes

Walkover

  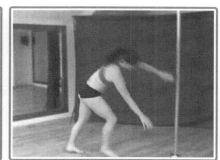

Also known as:

PDC Notes
Allow plenty of space around the pole.

Your Notes

Western Flag Cartwheel

Also known as:

Flag Cartwheel.

PDC Notes

Master the Western Flag invert first.

Your Notes

Western Flag X

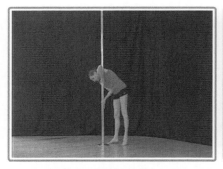  

Also known as:

Matrix X, Flag Split

PDC Notes

Your Notes

The Pole Dance Community

The Pole Dance Community (PDC) was established in 2009 to help self regulate the fast growing fitness pole dancing industry.

The PDC was the brainchild of husband and wife team Sid and Sam Remmer. Sam was aware of many pole dance schools who were not offering best practice to their students and so the PDC code of conduct for approved dance schools was created to form industry recommended standards for the tuition of pole dancing.

The PDC now approves individual instructors checking that they have the correct insurance as well as an up to date first aid qualification. All PDC approved instructors have a minimum of three years pole dancing experience and must comply with the strict PDC code of conduct e.g. no more than 3 students per pole.

Schools that have all their instructors approved can boast approved pole dance school status.

The Pole Dance Community is made of instructors from across the globe who each have an equal vote in how the community is run and how it evolves.

As instructors develop their career, we encourage and advise on continuing professional development and the positive promotion of fitness pole dancing.

The PDC has now implemented a scheme where dancers as well as teachers can monitor their progression using the Advancement and Accreditation Programme. Under the Advancement and Accreditation Programme pole dancers can undertake gradings to chart their progression and instructors can log their ancillary qualifications and experience.

The PDC also approves pole dance teacher training courses to identify clear pathways for the progression from student to instructor as well as offering pole dance specific insurance that includes both professional indemnity and public liability cover.

You can find out more about the Pole Dance Community and it members by visiting us online.

Pole Dancer Grading

Grading provides tangible feedback on your progress and gives you something to show off to your friends. It shows that you are learning a recognised sport at a reputable school, which should help dispel some of the misconceptions your friends and family may hold.

If you do decide to grade, we provide you with an official record book (your pole dancing passport) in which the instructor will validate your gradings. The book also has sections to record any competition attendance, master classes, first aid course completions etc. On request, we can also provide a certificate acknowledging your grading success.

You may progress through the grading levels and have your achievement recognised by all PDC Approved Schools, worldwide. If you moves location, you are able to continue your grading progression at any other PDC Approved School or via online gradings.

Do I have to train at a PDC Approved school to become a member?
No. You can train wherever you like – even at home - but your gradings must be taken either at a PDC Approved school or by video and sent to us.

We understand that many pole dancers train at home or do not yet have a PDC Approved school in their area and we do not want to exclude you.

How do I join in?
Either ask at your PDC Approved School (your instructor is authorised take your membership fee and pass the paperwork onto us), or if you train at home or at another school, you can email us for an info pack: info@poledancecommunity.com

or snail mail us at

The PDC Team
Dedicated to uniting the pole dance community

UK and world:
Pole Dance Community
5, Beaumont Avenue
Greenbank
Plymouth
Devon UK
PL4 8DX

USA only:
Pole Dance Community
445 South Halsted Street
Chicago Heights, Illinois 60411
USA

On-line Grading

If you want to do a pole dance grading and don't have a PDC Approved instructor near you then you can do an online grading - it's simple:

1. Video your warm up.

2. Choose any ten moves from your attempted grading level and demonstrate them individually.

3. Demonstrate the same ten moves, this time as part of a continuous pole dance routine.

4. Video your cool-down/stretches.

5. Upload the lot to YouTube and send us the link.

Your video will be assessed by a qualified PDC Grading Assessor who will respond with the outcome of your grading and also provide you with some written feedback.

You can find examples of on-line grading videos on our website - to help give you inspiration.

Good luck!

The PDC Team

10618748R00226

Printed in Great Britain
by Amazon.co.uk, Ltd.,
Marston Gate.